# AJAX, GOLDEN DOG OF THE AUSTRALIAN BUSH

# AJAX
## Golden Dog of the Australian Bush

*by*

MARY ELWYN PATCHETT

*Illustrated by*
ERIC TANSLEY

# THE BOBBS-MERRILL COMPANY, INC.
*Publishers*

INDIANAPOLIS                   NEW YORK

FOR BOB

BARBARA *and* WENTWORTH

# INTRODUCTION

**F**ROM away back as far as I can remember I lived in the strange, wild land of the Australian bush until I was fifteen and went to boarding school. My memory dates back to when I was two, when I was badly burned, and I never left my home for more than a few months until the time came for me to go to school.

Life on a cattle station, or ranch, was a lonely life, unless you were lucky enough to be one of a large family. But for me there were seldom other children to play with except when an occasional friend came to stay, or there were odd children around for a few weeks. I had an elder brother, but he went off to boarding school when I was very small and came home only for the long vacations twice yearly. So in a way I was very much alone.

In another way I was not alone at all. I had my dogs and a collection of Australian animals that ranged from a calf to a carpet snake called Kaa. My life was very busy, indeed, and full of adventures, for these are a part of the great, lonely land of Australia, with its rivers that may one week be just a string of muddy pools and the next a roaring torrent of yellow water seven miles wide.

It was a wild country and I loved it; I still do, from its gum trees with tall silver-and-mauve-streaked trunks, satin-smooth and shining in the moonlight, to the wide brown paddocks where the great herds of beef cattle roam and the little kangaroo rats make round nests from dried wisps of grass and come bounding out like fur-covered balls of gray when you disturb them, zigzagging like hares to throw off the coursing dogs; from the tree-fringed river, where the brown oblongs of resting platypuses dot the dark waters beneath the trees, to where the possums give their soft *ka ka kkkkaas* and the melancholy cry of a dingo fills the lonely moonlight and turns the vast emptiness of Australia into a land of ancient life, haunted by loneliness and hunger.

There were Christmases and birthdays for me just as there are for children everywhere—only my cake was smaller, and there were plates of bones and nuts and fruit for my guests! All year long there were regular happenings that were interesting to me and in which I could sometimes take part. There were polo and picnic race meetings, an occasional circus and buckjumping show and regular country shows for stock and agriculture.

These shows were very important to stations like my home, Gunyan, because we had a stud of purebred Herefords, and our champions competed at many shows during the year, and we always exhibited all the new, imported stock. During the 1914 war we had a fine Hereford bull shipped from England. The ship he was in was torpedoed, but the bull was rescued although its journey took months, and by the time it arrived it cost over £3,000—about $14,610. Then the very night the bull reached Gunyan, after all these adventures, it broke through three strong fences and got into a lucerne patch and died next day from overeating.

My father was not happy until another great, red, curly-haired beast arrived after a quieter voyage, and this one was stabled and groomed for the Inverell show. Show bulls have an enormous diet. Besides greenstuffs they get boiled pumpkin and oil cakes, a dozen fresh eggs daily and huge doses of castor oil which are supposed to make their coats curl!

Then when I was three I was allowed to compete in my first show. Two weeks beforehand the bulls were sent off in a huge van so that they would not walk the fat off themselves, and my fat brown pony Buck went along with them. I had spent weeks grooming him and feeding him lots of cracked corn and an occasional dose of the bulls' castor oil—which he did not appreciate at all.

My parents and I started for Inverell a couple of days before the show opened, and I was very upset because I was not allowed to take the three dogs I had then. One was an ancient fox terrier called Bumpy, another was a pretty black kelpie sheep dog, and there was a floppy pointer called Napoleon. However, I perked up and was most impatient for the second day of the show when the event for small children's ponies was to take place.

My great friend Lewis, who was the handyman round the station and always the person I depended on, brought Buck to me where I stood impatiently by the entrance to the show ring. Of course I rode without a saddle; there was just a cloth fastened on with a band to keep me clean. Buck was very gay—being so full of cracked corn—and he curvetted his portly body about the ring where other children bobbed about on their ponies, warming them up too.

I am told my father said to Lewis, rather uneasily, "I must admit I'm a bit worried about my daughter's sportsmanship. If Buck doesn't get the blue ribbon, she'll set up a terrible howl. She's sure to feel he's been insulted and that his feelings are hurt!"

Then the judge gave his orders and we all walked, trotted and cantered, and then lined up. In the end only Buck and a beautiful little black pony were left, and the judge walked forward and put the coveted blue ribbon round the black pony's neck. I'm glad to say I've only a hazy memory of what happened next, but I'm told I went very red in the face, leaned over and shouted at the judge, "Go away! Buck's the best— Buck *is* the best! Go away! You've hurt his feelings— take that nasty red ribbon away!"

Not very sportsmanlike! But the judge must have had children of his own, because he walked over and began talking to me. He put the red ribbon away in his pocket and took something else out which he fastened to the headband of Buck's bridle. I remember that I felt better. I felt still better when he took a wonderful object out of another pocket and fastened it on my small chest. I am told that I rode proudly round the ring, hastily followed by the real blue-ribbon winner from whom Buck had stolen all the applause, and then I cantered out of the exit gate and called to my parents to look at the object that was fastened to Buck's forehead.

"Look," I said proudly, "Buck's got a special prize for having the nicest expression! And look here—" I peered down at my meager chest—"*I* got this one for being a good rider!"

Buck's noble brow wore a heart-shaped ticket with a picture of the fat lady from the side show on one side and a fortune for those born in February on the other. On my chest was a beautiful blue disc with a magic inscription in gold that said "Champion Buff Orpington Hen."

My mother said, "Apparently the judge is a man who seldom empties his pockets!"

But I was delighted and said, "*I* think that the judge is the kindest man in the world!"

# CONTENTS

AJAX, GOLDEN DOG OF THE
AUSTRALIAN BUSH

# CHAPTER I

# ALGY

THROUGH all the adventures that happened in my childhood—and they ranged from helping to trap a horse thief to nearly losing my life through three wolves that had escaped from a circus—I had three faithful and deeply loved companions, and the first of these was Algy, who must have come to me when I was about five. Algy was a bulldog, and I had been promised a bulldog pup for a long time before my parents were able to get one for me, because in those days there were not many of them in Australia.

Algy was an entrancing pup. He was only a few weeks old when he came a long journey, all by himself, from the Queensland town of Warwick to Gunyan, near the border town of Texas. The river, the Severn, made the border between New South Wales and Queensland, so that if you wished you could practically stand with one foot in each state. Inglewood, the nearest rail station, was forty miles away, and as a truck was going to this station to collect some goods, my father arranged for Algy to be sent that day. He told the driver to leave plenty of room for the pup in the truck, as bulldogs were such big fellows.

I hardly slept a wink the night before Algy was due to arrive. In fact everyone was excited, for most of the station hands had never seen a bulldog either. Presently we heard the truck in the distance, and soon it pulled up in front of the house. The driver was grinning all over his face. "It's a good thing you sent the big truck, Boss," he called to my father. "He's a savage brute—and what a size!"

Dancing about at the back of the truck, I could hardly wait for it to be opened so that I would get the first glimpse of my bulldog. But the driver walked around from the front with something in his hand, saying, "Well, here he is!"

And there he was, the fattest, tiniest pup, all wrinkles, with a wee white, square-jawed face, floppy jowls and a black button of a nose—and he weighed just three pounds. Half of his head was a sort of blackish-gray, and the rest of him was white, and there was a permanent kink in his tail. I could hold him in one hand. When I put him on the ground he tried to sniff at an ant—his nose was so far back he almost had to stand on his head, and his wobbly legs gave way and he fell on his nose. He was the dearest baby.

Algy soon grew from a chubby pup into a great big dog, weighing nearly seventy pounds, with a massive chest and gentle, loving ways. He had plenty of affec-

tion from my family, yet his bulldog heart must have
had some emptiness our love could not fill. The first
time I realized this was when he trotted in from the
garden with a strange creature held very gently between his drooling jaws. He came up to me, looking
immensely pleased with himself, and put what he was
carrying very gently in my lap. It was a tiny tortoise!
Goodness knows where he had found it, perhaps on
the riverbank, perhaps on the dampish earth near the
water tanks. It was not much bigger than a penny and
quite black, and it reared its head and began scurrying
around my lap. I helped it to the floor and it ran a little
way, with Algy trying to head it off with his blunt nose.

When I picked it up Algy sat in front of me moving
his feet impatiently, obviously wanting to play with the
little creature, gazing upward and drooling in a way
which, if you did not know him, would make you think
he was longing to eat it. Finally we put it in a box with
wire netting over the top to keep the cats out. Then
Algy and I went to the river and brought back sand, and
finally made the tiny tortoise a little rock garden with
a pool and tiny pot plants and lots of stones to bask on.
We chopped up a little piece of raw meat and put it in
the pool, and the tortoise became very happy in its home.
I never saw it eat, but I expect it got insects off the
fresh greenery we gave it every day.

Algy would sit beside the box for hours, gazing at
his treasure, or woofing at me to take it out so that it

would run about as Algy leaped around and blew on it, which did not frighten the little thing in the very least. It grew very slowly, but finally it was big enough to have a small hole drilled in the edge of its shell so that it could be tethered beneath a tank to browse on the growing plants. It used to bob its head out at Algy's button nose when it wanted to play, and then retire into its shell house when it was bored with him.

Algy was older than Ben, my Australian terrier, who was the second of the three dogs who were my greatest friends. Algy was friendly with Ben's mother, Pam, long before Ben was born, looking more like a fat black mouse than a puppy. Algy peered into the basket at this little creature, then snorted so loudly that Pam jumped and growled. Finally he proceeded to settle down to adoring the naughty little pup and to doing his best in his loving, clumsy way to look after it. Between Algy and me I am afraid that Benny became a spoiled little monster. He bullied Algy from the moment he began to stagger about on fat, bandy legs, his portly tummy barely clearing the ground, and his sharp milk teeth taking nips at Algy's unprotected areas.

As Ben grew out of puppyhood, Algy still seemed to need something helpless to care for, and he adopted a series of the queerest babies. One morning at breakfast he came in from the garden and put a tiny, hairless, baby mouse down beside my porridge plate. It was rather bewildered and wet, but quite unhurt.

It used to bob its head out at Algy's button nose.

Algy's possum was one pet that I found for him, for it came to live in a tree outside the nursery window, where it slept most of the day and then got very lively toward the evening. I put milk and honey on the window ledge, and sat very quietly watching it running about the branches. After a long time Possy became so tame that I could pick it up. Algy was entranced with the possum, and once it got used to being blown on and to seeing the big smile split Algy's face almost in half, it really did not mind him at all.

Then one day I discovered it had a baby in its pouch. I was thrilled, and while it sat nibbling at the treats I brought it, it allowed me to put my finger in its pouch—very gently indeed—and to hook the baby out of it. It was almost more than Algy could bear not to be allowed to lick it.

Mother and baby possum spent a lot of time scrambling round the nursery and making possum faces at Algy. Then father possum moved into the tree, but he was wild and fierce, and I never tamed him. One day he fell into the slippery porcelain bathtub and could not get out again. He sat there making angry *kaaaa kakaka* noises, so I made a sort of rope ladder out of bath towels and fastened it to the window. Then I went out and closed the door so that father's dignity would be safe as he climbed up the towels to freedom. He probably went back to mother possum and told her I was a nasty, interfering little girl and that it was all my fault he had fallen into the bath in the first place.

Then Algy adopted a baby fox. It was only about four inches long except for its bushy tail. And what Algy stood from that imp of Satan! He never lost his temper with it, and always seemed disappointed when I put it to bed at night because it had to be shut up—foxes have so many enemies—and are themselves the enemy of so many. Finally the half-grown fox ran away and Algy mourned for a while. Then, though he seemed to forget his wild baby, I think he went to the riverbank sometimes on a moonlit night and played for a while with the nursling. I often missed him from beside my bed when I wakened at the quick, sharp yapping of a near-by fox.

One of his funniest adopted children was his duckling. Algy always followed me through the henhouses, and the hens were quite used to him. He would inspect all the old ladies who were sitting, sniffing at them and prodding them with his blunt nose so that their feathered bloomers rose in the air off the brood they were hatching. The hens were most indignant at his interference; naturally they considered their eggs were none of his business. They often must have wondered whose business they were anyhow, because these broody old girls used to find themselves with families of turkeys or ducks instead of chickens, and once a pelican, a most rare visitor, laid two eggs in a hen's nest, which unfortunately never hatched.

One evening we had gone the rounds and collected the eggs and returned to the house. Algy squatted in front of where I sat in a low chair, his eager eyes on me and the funniest expression on his face!

He was drooling a little from his big, flapping chops, and I said, "Algy! Whatever are you holding in your mouth?"

He gulped with excitement and must nearly have swallowed whatever it was, because he bent his head suddenly and it fell a few inches to the floor. It was an egg, and that eager look was guilt, for he knew that he must never touch an egg. The short drop broke it and inside the shell, its feathers wet and its little yellow bill cheeping with indignation, was a tiny duckling.

It must have been ready to crack its own shell, for it was quite strong. Algy put his nose near to it and gave a tremendous, excited snort—the gust hit the duckling and blew it back on its tail. It lurched to its small webbed feet and complained like Donald Duck himself! From then on the duckling was considered Algy's pet, and no one dreamed of eating it.

Unlike most small animals, my guinea pigs never got over their fear of Algy, and he gazed at them shivering with nervousness of him, while *he* trembled with anxiety to take care of them. The guinea pigs lived in an old-fashioned hencoop—the sort that has four corners, a wired top, and rests flat on the ground so that it can be moved to fresh grass every day. One day Algy managed to open the little door of the coop and to squeeze his big body inside. There he crouched, and I found the four corners stuffed with cowering guinea pigs while Algy pressed his square mug into the corner and bestowed large wet kisses on the terrified animals, because his nose was so square he could not get nearer to them than the tip of his tongue. It was one thing for him to get *in* the coop, but another to get him *out*. In the excitement of tipping the cage up to release Algy, I lost half the guinea-pig family.

Like most dogs Algy hated to be laughed at, and I always tried not to do it, but one day I just could not help myself. One sunny morning I found him in the garden gazing at a small, gay lizard that was running up and down the wooden edge of a flower bed. Algy was trying to creep up to it, puffing madly, while the lizard ignored him, peering about with bright eyes and making little darts at flies. When Algy could not bear it any longer he put his great paw down, softly, on the lizard's tail; but to his great astonishment the lizard scurried off leaving its tail under his paw. He never really recovered from the mystery of the whole thing, and he brought the tiny tail and put it in my lap, his face still expressing extreme wonderment.

Another day he came to me, woofing and blowing as he did when he had something to show me. So I followed him to the wild, shrub-tangled end of the garden, where he began to sniff at a glass bottle. I picked it up and inside was a large frill lizard, although the neck of the bottle was much too small for it to get out. We decided that the lizard must have crept into the bottle when it was tiny and that it lay there gorging on the flies and insects the bottle trapped, until it grew too big to get out. I have seen many ships in bottles, but only one lizard, and it raised its frill in the way that ship-bottle builders pull up the masts. We kept it for a day or two, then Lewis cut the neck off the bottle and released the lizard. It scuttled awkwardly away, and Algy watched it with the air of an elderly professor who has suddenly been confronted with a problem he could not solve.

Life went on very busily for me with all my pets to be cared for, as well as Algy's favorites. He must have been about two years old, and Ben only about a year, when we had the great adventure that was to give me the most beautiful, kingly, aloof dog I have ever known, the dog who saved my life at least twice. He was not bought. We did not breed him. I found him, and perhaps that helped to make him more my dog than any dog I have ever known before or since, and this is how it happened.

# CHAPTER II

# AJAX

USTRALIA is a land of violent contrasts. Sometimes the country suffers from a drought, and sometimes from rolling floods that carry away animals and houses, fences and even people. If you look at a map of Australia, you will see where a river makes part of the border line between New South Wales and Queensland, and halfway along this the river takes a sudden hairpin bend. The river has many names. Sometimes it's called the Severn, sometimes the Sovereign, and sometimes the Dumeresque. My home was right on a bend. Its name Gunyan was an aboriginal word for "running water." At times there was far too much running water, for the homestead stood with the river curving round it on two sides, and in a really great flood the water overflowed the banks and poured down on the house, like someone taking a diagonal short cut across a street corner.

I remember only one such flood, and while it was frightening and terrible, drowning animals and causing thousands of dollars worth of damage, I could not help finding it exciting, and it did give me the most

27

wonderful dog I have ever known—my golden giant,
Ajax.

It had been raining for weeks, both at my home and
far upriver where the small streams poured their rain-
fed waters into the main channel of the river, swelling
it into a great, thundering mass of water that broke its
banks and spread into a swiftly running torrent seven
miles wide. My father got news of the approaching
flood by telephone, and so we had time to make prepara-
tions to leave the homestead and move to higher land.

When my father said we must get ready to move,
the dogs and I were very excited. We were to take
tents and to go up to a hill about three miles from the
homestead, where we would be above the water however much it should rise. First of all, everything possible had to be put away, so we helped stack furniture
up in the big loft; then the car was driven up a ramp
onto a high veranda and chained there. It was no use
to us then, because the water in the small gullies lying
between us and the hill was already too deep to cross
in the car.

We had to make our trek in buggies and sulkies and
drays. Of course the station hands and their families
were coming too, and everybody rushed about, loading
drays, packing blankets and tents and food. My mother
and Nessie, who was our housekeeper now that I was
too big to have a nurse, packed cans of food and cut

sandwiches, gathered together changes of shoes and clothes, and finally said they were ready.

I'd packed most of my toys and staggered up to the loft with them; then I put the bridle on Buck, my bay pony, to lead him by, for I was going in the sulky with Lewis, who was a wonderful bushman, full of the sort of stories that children love to listen to. I was to lead Buck because Algy and Ben would not stay in the sulky without me, and Algy was afraid of water and would have to be carried over the streams, while Benny was really too small to follow if I rode Buck over the water-covered bush roads, full of rubbish and nasty deep potholes.

Finally we were ready, and the oddest-looking cavalcade you ever saw set off for the hilltop, which looked down on the muddy, rushing yellow torrent. Poor drowned animals floated and bobbed on the current. Great trees, uprooted as the water softened their earth-bound roots and toppled them into the flood, turned and twisted and bumped into tangles of fence posts and torn wires and jams of planks, where houses had been washed away and broken up in the fury of the waters, to be carried perhaps hundreds of miles downstream before being stranded by the receding river.

We reached the hilltop and the men began setting up the tents. The dogs and I seemed to be in everyone's way, so we walked down the hill to the edge of the river. It was a frightening sight, with water as far as my eyes could see, and once a small wooden cottage, all in one piece, went skimming by, twisting and turning in the current.

The dogs and I stayed for a long time at the edge of the water, watching it creep up on the stick my father had driven into the mud to test the rate the river was rising. Once we saw a huge gum tree, its twisted roots still earth-filled, towering above the water, hurtling along, twisting and turning and bumping other trees and logs. As the current swept it toward us I saw a long, evil head reared above the roots, like the carved figure on the prow of a ship. Thick coils twined about the roots, patterned as perfectly as if woven by a Persian carpetmaker, and I knew it was a very big carpet snake, a constrictor of the python type that sometimes grows to fifteen feet and more in length. It is harmless, but a great eater of hens and their eggs, and I knew that somebody was going to have an unwelcome visitor when the water finally left the tree stranded. However, that might be after a trip of hundreds of miles.

The dogs and I would have been quite happy to sit for hours by the water and watch the strange flotsam that went rushing by. But suddenly I became aware that not all the movement was on the water—the land around me was simply alive with creatures that had come out of their haunts to find high land out of reach of the river. There were frogs and spiders, centipedes and scorpions, lizards and snakes and goodness knows what else—all traveling up the hill toward our tents!

Algy and Ben were more fascinated than I was by all the creepy-crawlies, and barked madly at the frogs, trying to anticipate which way they would jump. That was all right, but I was afraid they might pounce on one of the more deadly creatures, so we went back up the hill. It wasn't much better up there, as the tents seemed to be carpeted with spiders already, as well as other oddities, but fortunately all these disturbed creatures seemed more interested in finding somewhere to hide than in rushing about or attacking animals. I felt that a great big dog like Algy should protect *me* from the creeping things, but he didn't like them himself. If he was having a doze and woke with one crawling over him, he would twitch his hide and whimper for me until I came along and knocked it off. Ben, who wasn't much bigger than a good-sized lizard himself, was much braver and had to be restrained from snapping at scorpions and spiders and those horrible, ghost-white centipedes that you never see until something like a flood has chased them from the rotten logs they live in, where apparently they never see the sun.

Most of the station livestock had been moved back into the hills several days before. Cattle are hopeless in floods; horses, even sheep, will try to swim, but cattle simply stand there until the water rises high enough to lift them off their hoofs, turn them over and drown them. So all the cattle in the river paddocks had been moved to higher lands, and the Hereford studs had their stablemen with them, well out of the reach of flood waters.

We had a campfire supper, and I was sent to bed almost as soon as it was dark. Algy and Ben lay on saddlecloths on the end of my camp stretcher. The whole place was wet and smelly and I was afraid of the whispering, rustling things that crawled about me in the dark, so I let Algy and Ben creep up on my bed and lie beside me, which in the ordinary way was strictly forbidden.

In the morning the water had fallen a few inches, and the dogs and I set out to explore. The small, teeming life did not seem so bad in the sunlight. The ground was squashy with wet, but the sun shone down with a cheerful warmth. We had gone out of sight of the camp and were walking among a lot of felled trees that had been chopped down in the summer. I walked cautiously around these, because I could not tell what might be lurking on the other side if I jumped over them.

I was just running round one when I heard a whining, scratching sound in it. I listened and heard it again, and so did the dogs, and Benny began to dig violently at one end of the log. I pulled him away because I was afraid of what he might find in there. Then I marked the log, called the dogs and we raced back to the camp to find Lewis.

Lewis brought an ax and began to chop carefully at the waterlogged bark. There was no sound from inside it, and I think Lewis thought that I had imagined the noise; then a chip of wood came away, and underneath it we could see a bright, golden gleam. Lewis made the opening wider, put in his hand and pulled out a long, yellow puppy, quite dead.

"Well, there you are," Lewis said. "I'm afraid we are too late—the little chap's dead."

"Oh, Lewis, how awful! But how long has he been dead?"

"About a day—perhaps more, I should think."

"You mean he hasn't just died this minute?"

"No, he's quite cold. He's been dead some time."

"Then he can't be the one I heard!" I shouted excitedly. "There must be another one in there!"

So Lewis began his careful chopping again, and sure enough another bright golden gleam appeared. He tore the soft wood away with his hands and my heart sank. There was no movement at all—apparently this little chap was as dead as his brother.

Lewis put his hand in to lift the pup and pulled it back, saying, "Ouch! He bit me, the little demon!"

"Oh, he's alive! He's alive!"

"He's alive all right, and he's got a mighty fine set of milk teeth."

Lewis put his hand back in the log more cautiously and lifted out another yellow pup, so nearly dead that it made little difference, but still with enough spirit to draw back his tiny upper lip and snarl at the big man holding him.

Lewis handed him to me, saying, "Here you are. I don't think he'll live—he seems all in—so you mustn't be upset if you lose him. Take him back to camp and get some warm milk from your mother, and wrap him up warmly."

The dogs were leaping up like mad things, each trying to look at the pup, sniffing and yelping until I had to scold them and make them keep down. Once the little fellow made a feeble snap at my hand; his teeth closed on the skin, but he hadn't enough strength in his jaws to break it. After that he seemed to lose consciousness, and his yellow head, small and babyish yet somehow full of character, lolled against my arm, and his yellow eyes stayed closed.

I walked back as quickly as I could and wrapped the baby in an old jersey, warmed some milk and forced it between his jaws. He swallowed a little and I lay down on my bed, holding him close to me for warmth and making the dogs stay at the foot, which annoyed them very much. All that day I fed the pup on milk every hour. If he wasn't any stronger, he certainly hadn't lost strength, and then I fed him every two hours all through the night. My mother wanted to help me, but I wanted to care for him all myself, so she let me.

The next morning the pup was brighter, and I was half dead with sleepiness! Once he tried to struggle up, and snarled and gave quite a brisk snap at my hand. I left him asleep on my bed when I went to get my breakfast, and rushed into the tent again when I heard a violent yelp from Benny. I discovered that Master Ben, taking advantage of my absence, had been nosing around the pup, and had had his black button of a nose well nipped for his pains.

That afternoon I was very sleepy, so after I had fed the pup I lay down beside him and went off to sleep. I must have slept very soundly, for when I woke the pup was not there, and the jumper I had rolled round him trailed from the bed to the ground. I jumped up and hurried to the tent flap, pushed it aside, and there I saw a sight I shall never forget.

Outside on the wet ground I saw a circle of dogs. In it were Algy and Ben and the sheep and cattle dogs belonging to the stockmen. In the center of the ring stood my tiny, savage, golden pup. He swayed on his legs, but a faint, ominous growl came from the small golden chest. As he grew older this faint ghost of a growl turned into the deep, shuddering thunder of the fighter. His lips were drawn back, and his brilliant yellow eyes were filled with flickering pink lightnings. This wee, starved pup was defying a dozen full-grown dogs in his lonely, friendless world. My heart went out to him as I watched; his hind legs gave way and he sat down, but he still kept his head high and rumbled his tiny defiance of the crowd.

I couldn't bear it any longer, he was so alone. I stepped forward and picked him up. His sharp eye-teeth broke the skin on my hand and drops of blood welled out. I left my hand in his jaws, and he looked up at me uncertainly. I stroked his head with my other hand, and he opened his jaws. I kept on stroking him and presently he licked the salty blood off my hand, with a wondering expression in his eyes.

Then I held him against my face and whispered to him, "Do you know that you're *my* dog—that you're my Ajax, the bravest of the brave?"

He licked my cheek and that ended our first battle of wills. I had won—he was my dog, my Ajax, forever.

CHAPTER III

# AJAX RESCUES ME

ONCE the flood began to go down, the river and the little creeks that fed it dropped rapidly. Actually I had had Ajax for only two days when my father decided that it would be safe to begin the trek home. So we packed up everything once again and started off home, I holding Ajax on my knee and the other two dogs sitting jealously—Algy at my feet, Benny on the seat between Lewis and me.

It wasn't at all a pleasant drive. There were only patches of dry road, and all sorts of things were hidden in the watery holes and pools, logs and washed-away earth. I had my work cut out trying to hold on to all three dogs as we went bumping along.

When we reached the homestead we found it in a horrible mess of mud and rubbish, but safe. An appalling smell hung over everything. The river had risen to nearly two feet high in the house, and the floors were a foot deep in smelly mud and dead crawlies—but not all of them were dead either! Everyone worked at shoveling the mud out until hoses could be put on. Finally it was pretty clean, but it stayed damp and beastly for days. And as for the garden, it was absolutely ruined. In the end the river mud did it a lot of good, the way that the overflowing Nile feeds the crops, but nearly everything had to be replanted.

Ajax grew stronger every day, and soon he could lap up his milk; then his yellow eyes would narrow to slits of ecstasy as he drank. When he got a little larger and stronger on his legs, Algy longed to play with him. He would bowl the pup over and push him along with his nose, while Ajax went on with frenzied snappings and snarlings. Then Algy blinked at the ridiculous pup, seemed to shrug his big shoulders and probably gave up the effort. When Ajax snapped at Benny, Benny snapped back at him, and then there were such squealings and yelpings of rage on both sides that I had to separate them.

Ajax grew into a tremendous dog. He never played with other dogs and he just tolerated humans. He seemed to get the exercise his huge frame needed on long, nightly hunting trips from which he would return and throw himself down beside my bed until morning. I was the one thing he loved, and he hardly took his deep yellow eyes off me. I hated to go anywhere without him, for when I went away he was filled with savage despair.

In a couple of years he grew nearly as big as a calf, and his coat was a glorious orange-golden color. We decided that his mother must have been a dingo—one of those clever, savage Australian wild dogs—and his father, most likely, was a big kangaroo dog. Kangaroo dogs are like giant greyhounds, very fast on their feet, with great deep chests and bony, intelligent heads.

When Ajax was three, my family took a house at the seaside for the summer. I was excited about this, but miserable at the thought of leaving the dogs behind, especially Ajax who would be so unhappy without me. Nevertheless I had to go.

When we arrived at a quiet cove below Sydney called Half-Moon Bay, I was delighted with the bungalow, which was built high above the ground with a sort of open-air playroom beneath with a table-tennis table and other joys, and all around it a big, high-fenced garden. The wire-netting fence was there to keep away marauding dogs. The house overlooked the beach and the splendid, wild waters of the Pacific, with waves like emerald galleons topped by wind-torn white sails.

The morning after we arrived, after spending nearly a week in Sydney on the way down, I was plunging about in the surf when a "dumper"—that's a big wave full of churning undertow—caught me, knocked me down and then landed me on the beach in a smother of sand and water. When I got my breath and opened my eyes, I was knocked down again—by Algy and Ben!

They scrabbled and yelped and smothered me. Algy, in moments of excitement, always imagined he was a tiny puppy again and wanted to sit on my knee. So there he was, knocking me down and trying to sit on me at the same time!

When I managed to look up, Lewis was standing behind me, his dark face creased with laughter.

I called out, "Oh, Lewis, how lovely—where's Ajax?"

"He's waiting in the garden. I didn't know how he'd take to the beach if there was a crowd here. I didn't realize it would be so quiet——"

"But how did you get here?"

"Well, I think you have to thank Ajax. I had an awful job with him after you left. He kept starting out to find you. So I wired to your father after a day of this, and got my orders to drive the truck down and bring all the boys along. We've covered about five hundred miles in the last four days. Look!"

He broke off and pointed to where, against the sky line on the edge of the sand, stood a colossal, orange-colored dog. The dog stood motionless for a second, and then I called "Ajax!" and he left the bank. He didn't seem to jump; he just launched himself into space, and the next instant I was knocked flat and Ajax stood over me, his feet planted on each side of my body, his serious, savage eyes gazing into mine. The wild light died out of them, and I put my hand up to his muzzle.

He gave a little whine, strange from such a great, gaunt creature, and I think the only whine I ever heard him give. Then he put his head down and licked my face. I put my arms around his neck and pulled myself up, then we all went home to breakfast.

Each of the dogs had a different approach to the surf that curled and hissed up the long crescent of coarse, golden sand. Benny rushed at it, biting the bubbles and wobbling ludicrously behind as he backed away from a wave, and he always thought the waves were chasing him up the beach.

Algy mumbled in his chops, then put his head on one side until his expression said quite plainly, "Somebody's fooling me. I *won't* go in that great big bath!" Finally he licked at the froth, paddled a little where the sand was wet from the spent waves, decided that it was quite harmless after all and settled down to enjoy himself. The small crabs fascinated him—he sniffed at them, then leaped back wildly as they nipped his nose. His chops flapped with slapping sounds that startled the crabs and always made me laugh.

Ajax looked neither to right nor left. He followed me a few steps into a rushing wave, breasted it with me, and calmly followed into the deep water and swam beside me as if he had done it all his life. I think that Ajax really loved the water apart from his wish to stay near to me. He was a very strong swimmer, and would tow me along whenever I put my hand on his neck. Sometimes he let me swim by myself, but he always lay on the sand and watched until I came out again.

One fine morning I woke early and decided to go for a swim. Ajax was off on one of his prowls, and I could hear Ben and Algy quarreling about something at the back of the house, so I decided to trick them and slip off alone. The sun was still below the horizon, but it made a track of light from the beach to the end of the sea-filled world. It was high tide and the sea looked oily and heavy, with no waves to speak of. I decided that there was probably a heavy undertow and that I must be careful. I kicked off my sandals and waded in. The sudden, crisp, cool shock of the water was wonderful, and I began swimming.

Presently I thought I was far enough from the shore and turned to swim in, but I couldn't. I could feel the strong grip of the water drawing me away from the beach. I knew I mustn't panic. I let myself float for a moment to regain my strength, and was alarmed to find that I was being carried seaward even more swiftly than I thought.

I was very afraid. I couldn't fight the undertow, and the sea was so deep and undisturbed that it was likely to attract the deadly gray nurse sharks. It was a nasty thought that those powerful, hungry fish might be cruising near to me quite unseen. I grew more and more afraid. I tried to control myself, but as the weakness of weariness crept over me the terror mounted. I turned my head toward the shore and called despairingly, "Ajax! Ajax!"

I called despairingly, "Ajax! Ajax!"

43

It seemed minutes afterward, but it could only have been seconds, when I heard feet thudding on the beach. I turned my head, and bounding across the pale gold of the early-morning sands was the darker golden shape of Ajax.

He sprang from the hard-packed sand at the edge of the water like something launched from a catapult, and then I could see his great head moving strongly toward me across the terrifying waste of water. In a minute or so the head came nearer to me, and as I put my arm across his neck he turned toward the shore, and I saw my father and Lewis there. They were struggling to launch the little boat we kept dragged up on the dry sand out of reach of the tide.

Even Ajax, strong swimmer though he was, could make no headway against the terrible pull of the undertow. He could barely hold his own with my added weight dragging at him. I was too exhausted to help, and could only hang on and try not to hamper the dog too much. I thought I could hear my father's voice shouting encouragement, but I felt that even Ajax's great strength was waning. His shoulders moved more slowly, though his gallant heart kept him trying.

I don't remember much more, although I became conscious that the boat was beside me, and I had only one idea fixed firmly in my mind: I must not let go of Ajax. My father told me afterward that they just could not pry my hands loose from Ajax's neck, and that they had to pull the great dog and me into the boat in one piece. At one stage they decided to tow us in, but they, too, thought of the sharks; so with a great struggle they finally hauled the dog in with me attached.

When we reached the beach my father rolled me in his coat, made a sand pillow for my head and told me to lie there quietly. For once in his life Ajax lost his aloofness. No human face could have expressed greater anxiety for a loved one. He padded softly round me, every now and again putting his big head down close to mine, licking my hand, and finally lying close beside me.

In a few minutes I felt better. Then my father told me that he and Lewis decided on an early-morning swim too, and as they were leaving the house they heard a rush of feet and saw Ajax tear down the garden and sail over the fence. They decided that this must mean that I was in some sort of danger, and they ran after the dog. When they reached the beach they could see Ajax's head far out in the path of sunlight, and beyond it a small dot that they knew must be mine. They tore for the boat, and it was then that Ajax reached me and I saw them over his head.

The rest of the vacation was heavenly. Benny, especially, was fascinated by the life in the deep potholes studding the rocks. These holes were round and quite deep, for they are ground out by the tides swirling stones round and round in the same places for years until the holes are formed, and finally these become the homes of all sorts of sea creatures.

Crabs were always fascinating mysteries to Ben as well as to Algy. He would poke his nose into thick bunches of seaweed, give a surprised yell as something nipped him, then back away. Then he would creep back cautiously, unable to control his curiosity, and retire again with a shriek of surprise and a backward bound, and sometimes he would have a small, outraged crab fastened to his sharp nose! Then Benny would squint down it, fill his lungs for a colossal yelp—and as likely as not the crab would drop off. At that, Benny staggered back on his haunches, looking for the back, or nonnipping end of this strange creature—and the crab scuttled off sideways!

Oh, it was fun! And even Ajax showed amazement at one friend I made. I was gazing into a tiny rock pool, when I noticed what I took to be a piece of strange, speckled seaweed. I touched it gently with my finger and it curled over the tip—I was holding hands with a baby octopus! I peered into the pool and could see its eight little arms waving about in the water, each one just a few inches long. Its queer little face seemed merely a pair of eyes and a strange sort of tiny beak. I put my hand into the water and managed to detach it gently from its rock. It wound its tentacles round my hand. The dogs were wild with excitement, each wanting to look, and I laughed when the dignified Ajax jerked his head away in a far from dignified manner when the baby touched his nose.

Algy was affectionate, as he was to all small creatures, and Benny belligerent, and he had to be scolded and kept in his place. The little octopus wasn't at all frightened, merely active. He untwined himself from my hand and ran up my arm and over my shoulder, perched there a minute and then ran down my back and dropped onto the rocks. Once on a rock he drew himself up high on his eight arms and bustled back into the pool, just like a Walt Disney octopus.

Those lazy, sun-filled days were full of unusual excitements for an inland-bred child, for even the finding of an old plank, washed up in the tide and covered with goose-necked barnacles, was thrilling. The dogs were madly excited over the barnacle-covered plank, and barked and bounded about it as the myriad heads waved about in their aimless manner, like the result of a badly done hair-do. I think the plank looked to the boys like one long and very peculiar animal!

The summer ended at last, and as our return road home meant going through Sydney we stayed a few days for my mother to do some shopping. It was not easy to manage the dogs in a town, for none of them had ever worn collars, and they had not a clue about traffic. So it meant that nearly all their exercise, in fact their whole life, was lived on the roof of the hotel. My family had always stayed in this particular hotel and they were very good about the dogs, so it really was not too difficult as it was only for a few days anyhow.

It was during this stay that we all acquired a new friend, so it was worth a little inconvenience.

CHAPTER **IV**

# KIKO

**D**URING the few days we stayed at the Metropole with the dogs, my mother was busy interviewing possible governesses for me. I did not think much of this idea because I never had had regular lessons. And as I could read and write quite well by the time I was five I hated the idea of having to learn anything else! My father and I would spend hours at the zoo, Taronga Park, and as I loved the monkeys I used to get the keepers to let me follow them into the various cages so that I could nurse the gibbons, give the chimpanzees their milk and take the orangutans for walks.

It was while I was doing this that I made a wonderful friend, an old sea captain who loved monkeys too. He used to bring consignments of animals from the East for the Australian zoos, and when I met him he was visiting the last batch of monkeys he had brought. Usually these little tropical monkeys die on the voyage down, because the nights at sea are cold for monkeys born in the steamy, tropical forests of Malaya. The captain hated to see the poor little beasts huddled together and very miserable, for monkeys get seasick, and they develop pneumonia very easily.

So as soon as his ship put to sea, the captain made all his sailors sew little pajamas for the monkeys. The tough sailors were disgusted at being turned into monkeys' tailors, but the captain insisted. And then when the pajamas were finished the sailors had to catch the monkeys every evening and put them on, and then undress them every morning! The monkeys bit and scratched, but every evening the captain inspected the forty little monkeys in forty little suits of pajamas, and said good night to them. As a result of this care none of the monkeys died—but the sailors were very glad when the voyage was over.

The captain came to lunch at the hotel with us one day. Afterward I took him up to meet the dogs, and even the aloof Ajax could not help liking him. Then he and I went off to walk round the town. As we came out of the hotel we heard the sound of rollicking music in the street, and saw a young Italian turning the handle of a barrel organ. On it was the smallest, most miserable-looking monkey. It had a belt and heavy chain round its waist, and it wore a wisp of a dirty red coat and a silly cap above its pinched little face. It was shivering with cold, for it was May, and May in Sydney can be very cold indeed. The captain gave me a penny to give the little monkey, and it put out its little paw and ignored the penny, just clinging to my finger.

The Italian went on turning his hurdy-gurdy, and I lifted the monkey in my arms and it pressed its shivering body against me for warmth while it cheeped softly in the saddest way. It was one of the many varieties of capuchin monkey, the captain said. But it looked like a squirrel with its long tail, which should have been fluffy but which was very moth-eaten-looking. Most of the monkeys on barrel organs have rather wiry fur with a greenish tinge, and stand upright and have tails like whips. This one was small and soft and very miserable.

I was nearly in tears when I put the little thing on the top of the organ and it tried to creep back to me again. The captain gave the boy some money and told him to buy the monkey a warmer coat, and we walked on.

We heard a voice calling us and turned to find the Italian walking after us, while in the distance the monkey crouched, trying to huddle itself together against the cold wind. The man wanted the captain to buy the monkey, but the captain refused. The Italian persisted, so I walked back and picked the monkey up again, and stood sheltering it from the cold wind.

Presently both men came back. The Italian spoke to me, smiling so that his teeth shone in the sunlight. But I did not care. I only wanted to keep the monkey warm.

He unfastened the heavy chain and put the end in my hand. "You taka da monk," he said, still grinning.

I looked toward the captain, who was smiling. "It's your monkey now," he said.

"But doesn't he want it any more?"

"He's going away——"

"The gentleman, he buya da monk," the man explained.

"Oh! Is it for *me*? Do you really mean it belongs to me?" I was too excited to believe it.

"It does—if your mother'll let you have it."

"Oh, thank you!" I said. "I do love it!"

I pulled my coat round the little monkey and we went back to the hotel and found my mother writing letters. She was rather horrified at my cuddling such a dirty little thing in its horrible rag of a coat, but I could see how upset she was at its neglected condition. She went upstairs and put on her hat and brought down a warm scarf to wrap around the little monkey. Then we got in a cab and set off for the vet's.

The vet said there was nothing wrong with my monkey except neglect. He took off the belt and chain and found its middle sore and raw, so he took the little thing away, and in about a quarter of an hour he returned with a much cleaner monkey, bandaged round the tum. We bought a light belt and chain, and then some grapes and bananas. As we could not buy a coat for the monkey we bought some soft flannel, and my mother said she would make one.

Then we went back to the hotel, wondering how we

would smuggle the little fellow in, but pretty sure that the housemaid who did our rooms would not give us away. My father came in and said that finding a monkey did not surprise him—he always expected to find one new pet whenever he came back. The captain named my new pet Kiko, and we bought it a basket for a bed so that I could carry him about, onto the roof and into the parks.

I knew the dogs would not hurt him, although Master Ben, who was used to being the smallest pet, could be quite cross if I made a fuss over an even smaller gentleman. I certainly wondered how Kiko would take to them!

I was due for a big surprise, although I was right about Benny—he was a little jealous. Algy loved Kiko at once, but Ajax, who was so indifferent, was as nearly affectionate to Kiko as it was possible for him to be. It was to Ajax that Kiko always went whenever he was with the three dogs, and Ajax liked it. He would stretch out in the sunlight, pretending to doze and looking quite beautiful with his orange coat giving back the sunlight, and Kiko would creep between his big forelegs, right up under his chin, while Ajax nuzzled him as he never did any other creature.

We all enjoyed the long trip home, although I did not want to leave the captain. Kiko soon lost his sore middle and climbed about the car, slept on my lap, or played with the dogs quite happily through the long days of motoring over about five hundred miles of bad roads.

When we reached home Kiko took up residence in my nursery. He seldom climbed like other monkeys, but he would run about the floor with his bushy tail down between his hind legs and curling up in front of his chest like a tiny sleigh with a scroll-like prow. When he wore his belt and chain and it got in the way, he picked the chain up in one velvet-soft paw and lifted it around, as a lady might lift a train.

Kiko soon grew a beautiful, silky coat, and he would croon and cheep happily to himself all day long. He loved being made much of, and developed an enormous appetite for such a tiny creature. He had very nice table manners and would take a grape gently from your palm, patting it with his other paw as if to say thank you.

I believe he had a happy life. He was a busy little fellow and had his own toy box. At night I would put his toys away; in the morning he would take them out again. His favorite toy was a scrap of carpet which he would tack down with thumbtacks, hammered in with a little hammer taken from my brother's tool chest. At night I would pull it up. In the morning he would start afresh. He never got tired of it and he never hit his thumb! When he got tired of playing, Ajax would lie down while Kiko crept over him until *he* got tired; then they both went to sleep.

As no suitable governess had turned up for me, I had

a reprieve. I always knew that eventually I would have to go to boarding school, and I hated the idea, but fifteen still seemed an awfully long way away. So I went on happily enjoying my dogs and Kiko and looking forward to the show, which that year was to be combined with a circus and many side shows, and was due a few weeks after we arrived home.

CHAPTER V

# WE CLAIM WALTZING MATILDA

MOST bush excitements are connected in some way with horses. In Australia you do not learn to ride, you just *do,* and you begin when you are so young that there seems there never was a time when you did not ride. The English form of riding is much more stylized than Australian. In England and America you learn how to sit and how to hold your hands and feet and what to do if your horse makes an unexpected move. The English-style saddles, too, are less flat and slippery than Australian saddles, and the stirrup leathers are shorter. Australians ride by balance and instinct, keeping their hands low because it seems the most effective way in which to cope with a horse's mouth. The horses seldom trot, but break straight from a walk to a canter, and for long distances they go at a rather horrible jog.

We never rode for enjoyment, except in shows. Riding was simply a method of working and getting from one place to another, and the stockmen simply could not understand it at all when our English friends used to want to go for a ride!

A professional stock breaker came around the station at least once a year. In the middle of the cattle yards there is always a round yard with a tall, strong fence, for it is in this yard that the breaker rides the wild horses.

Of course I adored this, and used to sit on the top rail so as to have a front seat, holding Ben beside me, while Algy and Ajax stayed below. Then the breaker sprang onto the wild horses and rode them bucking and snorting around the yard in a whirl of dust and sweat, until the poor beasts, broken indeed, came trembling to a standstill. It was a cruel method, but with so many horses to break in, and so few men to do it, it could not be helped. Of course thoroughbred horses got a much better deal and a slower breaking-in, but with the mass of half-wild horses brought from the far paddocks, and not very different from the wild horses which are called brumbies, these hard, rapid methods made them ridable but never really tame or pleasant to ride.

Every year, too, the foals were brought in for branding, and what a mob of wild, leggy little creatures they were! Sometimes one of the stockmen would put a rope halter on a foal and hoist me up onto its back. Then when it bucked madly and I shot into the air, one of the other men would catch me. I loved this, and of course it was quite safe with the men looking after me, and it went on until I got too heavy to catch.

Naturally, with horses playing such a big part in everyone's life, any entertainment like a buckjumping show had to be very good indeed. One of these shows was more famous than any of the others, for the star horse was considered the most savage buckjumper in the country and the man who rode him was an unbeatable rider. So when it got around that this man, Billy Weight, and his horse Bobs were coming to the show we looked forward to it very much indeed. There were to be other side shows and the inevitable merry-go-round. Strange to think that bush children who rode so many real horses were so excited about climbing onto little wooden horses and being whirled round and round to the hurdy-gurdy music of the calliope! Of course you have to remember that most bush children had not seen a train, or even a tall building, or the sea, and these little shows held all the glamour and excitement of the year for them.

When this particular show opened, my father and I drove to it in a car that was rather like one of today's station wagons, but we just called it the truck. The sides were netted in so that the dogs could ride in there, and we took them nearly anywhere with us. They hated staying at home, and in the truck they would simply lie down and sleep when we left them.

When we reached the show my father and I started

around to the side shows, leaving the dogs in the truck. We laughed at ourselves and each other in the distorting mirrors, and I had a ride on the merry-go-round. We called on an old friend, the snake handler, who was wading about the snake pit in a pair of pink knit bootees, through which, he claimed, the snakes could not get their fangs.

Then it was time for the buckjumping show, and it seemed that the tent held every bushman for miles around, because in a country of fine riders Billy Weight was considered the finest of them all. He was a half-caste (these men are often wonderful riders) and Bobs, his horse, was unique. Real buckjumpers are very rare. Lots of horses buck in a way, but it is mostly what is called pigrooting. They put their heads down, arch their backs and jump along in a stiff-legged way. This is fairly hard to sit, but the *real* buckjumper is almost unridable, for it gives a sort of twist to its body in mid-air, all four feet off the ground. Bobs was the real thing, and some of the finest riders in Australia could not sit him.

Inside the buckjumping tent the ring was quite a small one of trodden-down earth, surrounded by a strong rail fence to keep the bucking horses from breaking through—this sometimes happened anyhow! The tent was lighted by smoky flares. There were no seats, everybody stood, and the tent was packed with tough, leathery bushmen waiting to see this rider who was supposed to be better than themselves. Most of the crowd knew my father, and they let me wriggle through their legs until I was beside the ring.

In films of American rodeos the horses are saddled and mounted in a horse-sized yard we call a crush, so that they cannot plunge about. But that is not the way we do it in Australia. There the saddle may be put on in the crush, and it is a slippery *poly* saddle without kneepads, something like a large racing saddle. Then the gate of the crush is opened, the horse dashes out and is mounted free in the ring.

I saw Bobs come charging into the ring. He was a great bay, eighteen hands high, glistening with sweat and fury. Then Billy Weight slipped into the ring. He was a small man, lithe as a cat, an old felt hat in one hand and soft-soled sneakers on his feet. Bobs reared and plunged, and when Billy was ready he ran a few steps across the ring and sprang high on that twisting, rolling demon's body. He shouted and hit the horse with his old hat, and the intensity and savagery of the horse's tremendous twisting leaps were thrilling to watch. The bushmen around me *knew* how great a rider this man was.

When Billy thought Bobs had had enough he slipped to the ground, the gates opened, and Bobs charged out again. It was as though a bolt of lightning had left the ring; once again it was just a dimly lighted earth-floored circle.

He shouted and hit the horse with his old hat.

After that we left the buckjumping tent and noticed a sign above another tent announcing "Boxing Kangaroo." My father was not very keen on this, he did not like kangaroos being made to box; but I was very insistent, so he let me go in. There were not many people in the tent, and on one side of the little roped-in ring was a biggish lavender kangaroo. It stood dejectedly there, and its coat was dull and patchy in the dim light, so I walked over and rubbed its ears. It pressed its head against my hand, and I thought how gentle the big animal was.

Then the showman made some sort of speech to which I did not listen. A man stepped into the ring and the showman tied boxing gloves onto his hands. Then he came over to where I was with the kangaroo and began to put another pair of gloves onto the animal, which pulled away and seemed frightened. The man growled at it and held on roughly.

I said, "It doesn't want those things on its hands. Why don't you leave it alone?"

The man laughed unpleasantly. "If she don't fight, I lose me money. Come on, you," and he pushed the kangaroo into the middle of the ring. The kangaroo's arms looked so thin and its little paws were lost inside the big gloves, but the showman pushed it in front of the man it was to fight. It balanced on its tail, and the man hit it on the side of the head. The poor thing moved back, the showman shouted, and the man slapped it again as it moved backward in clumsy, frightened hops.

My father took my arm and said, "You must come away. You don't want to watch this."

Suddenly I was furious with the people standing around who did want to watch this poor creature, and I could not stand it. I pulled away from my father and ducked under the railing into the ring, and ran between the kangaroo and the man, shouting, "You leave her alone, you big bully!"

The man laughed and so did the crowd.

I was terribly angry and went on shouting. "You wouldn't laugh if Ajax and Algy were here. Ajax! Algy! Here! Here, boys!"

My father stood by the ring, watching that I did not get myself into real trouble. He hated cruelty too, but because I was always rushing into things, he decided that I must learn not to begin anything I could not finish by myself.

The showman tried to pull me away from the kangaroo, but I shut my eyes and hung on, shouting for the dogs. How the dogs got out of the truck I will never know, but suddenly the crowd in the tent parted and Ajax reached me in one bound over the low railings. His eyes flickered with red fire, and the deep, shuddering thunder in his chest sent the showman scurrying back from me.

Then Algy galumphed into the ring, panting and growling, followed by Benny, who was yapping his head off and making more noise than the other two put together, although he was so tiny.

The showman and the boxer backed out of the ring and looked nervously at the dogs. My father just watched. He knew that Ajax would not move unless someone touched me—and no one was likely to do that while the great dog stood beside me, still as a statue except for the deep breaths rumbling in his chest. Algy stood squarely on the other side of me, great head down, snorting and rumbling, and Ben danced around in a frenzy of excitement, not knowing in the least what it was all about.

"Don't you *dare* touch my kangaroo!" I shouted at the showman.

And the man shouted back, *"Your* kangaroo! I like that! I'll show yer——" He took a step toward me— and Ajax took a step toward *him.* He moved back hastily.

"Hi, mister! he called to my father, "call yer dawgs off, will yer? Yer little girl's spoilin' my show."

My father said, "Better my little girl than the police. You know well enough what you'd get if anyone reported the condition of that kangaroo—there'd be no show at all."

Then someone in the crowd shouted, "We've paid our money!"

"I don't care. No one's going to hurt my kangaroo!" I shouted back, and then the crowd began to laugh, and ve must have looked very funny, the three dogs, the kangaroo and I, all bunched together in the center of the ring, and the angry showman not daring to come near us. I began taking the gloves off the kangaroo while Ajax and Algy kept guard.

The whole thing ended by my father buying the kangaroo. Then the crowd moved back to let us pass, and we, accompanied by the kangaroo, all walked out to the cheers of the crowd.

When we got outside my father said to me, "You know, these wars you get yourself into are very expensive for me."

"Oh, I know, Daddy. But we couldn't leave the poor thing."

"What would you have done if the dogs hadn't been able to get to you, and if the owner hadn't agreed to sell—and if I hadn't been there to buy it for you?"

Well, there were no answers to that, so as the kangaroo did not seem at all afraid of the dogs we put her in the back of the truck and christened her Matilda.

Algy adored her. He was sure he had saved her, and she became his own special thing. Ajax did not care about anything so long as I was safe, and as for Benny—he might have bought Matilda with his own money, from his air of personal triumph.

Matilda made friends with everyone, and soon grew fat and sleek, nibbling about the garden and playing games with Algy, which she always ended by prodding

him with the long toe on her hind foot. Algy spen
happy hours lying in the shade while Matilda move
about him, nibbling grass blades; in fact, the who
thing proved to be a beautiful friendship which bega
when Algy, like a brave knight of old, rescued a beau
tiful maiden. And she *was* beautiful, with soft eyes an
small, helpless hands—and a very long and very mus
cular tail!

CHAPTER VI

# CIRCUMSTANTIAL EVIDENCE

YOU might think that with Kiko in possession of my nursery, and Matilda hopping about the garden, that winter would have been an enjoyable one. But it began with my grandmother getting ill and my mother going off to look after her, and then it went on to bring me great sorrow over Ajax.

In the bush the greatest crime a man can commit is to steal stock, and the very worst thing any dog can do is to kill stock. That is why the Australian wild dogs—dingoes—are destroyed so relentlessly, for they are the worst of all killers. They kill because it amuses them, and on a moonlight night one dingo might kill several hundred sheep, ripping them up the belly and leaving the poor brutes to die.

Because my home was a cattle station, dingoes were not quite such a menace to us, and probably we did not go to quite such lengths to destroy them as the sheepmen did. That is why I so often heard their mournful howling as I lay in bed on moonlit nights. Dingoes are very clever—some bushmen say that they can count up to five or six. Sometimes one man will camp out in the bush, all alone, with nothing else to do but try and destroy probably *one* dingo.

The cows of our dairy herd, which supplied the milk for the station, were always separated from their calves at night so that they would have plenty of milk in the morning. The calves were penned into the milking yard, and the cows grazed about outside.

One morning Frank, the man who did the milking, had risen early as he always did. It was a crisp winter morning, and when he reached the yard he was surprised to see the calves huddling together in one corner, instead of frisking about as usual. They were calling loudly for their mothers. On the ground at the side of the yard farthest from the calves were four others, four little bundles of red and white hide, and in the muddy ground around them was the imprint of huge paws. Outside the fence the mothers pressed against the rails and mooed unhappily.

Frank came straight back to tell my father. I heard them talking, and we waited for Lewis while Frank called him, then we all started for the yard together. My father wanted me to stay behind, but I would not. In my heart I was terribly afraid, and I had to go and look for myself.

The railings round the yard were of old, rotted wood, and the killer dog had leaped the top rail instead of crawling underneath, as most domesticated dogs would have done. Although the killing looked like the work of a dingo, Lewis thought that there was one very strange thing about it: dingoes kill sheep, they don't kill calves unless they are very hungry. And this one hadn't been hungry, for the calves were untouched except for the one savage slash which is the dingo's trademark when he kills for the sole joy of killing. And besides, he must have run right past a mob of sheep, which were kept for mutton and were grazing in the same paddock as the milking cows.

There were paw marks in the soft ground near the fence and a white mark on the top rail, where a bit of bark had been ripped off when the dingo leaped over and landed on the soft ground inside the yard. The rest of the marks were from the terror-stricken rushing-about of the calves, a confusion of prints, sharp little hoofmarks and heavy pad marks. We all stood silently looking down at one big, clear, paw mark.

Then Frank spoke slowly, with a worried look at me. "I never seen a dingo with paws *that* big. It looks like . . ." He hesitated a moment.

"Like what, Frank?" my father asked.

"I don't like to say it, Boss, but there's only one dog around here big enough to make them marks."

My father glanced at me, I couldn't speak. Ajax stood beside me, a great, golden statue of a dog, with proud, aloof eyes.

"No, not Ajax!" I said and put my hand on the big head. Ajax moved against me and his throat rumbled, as if he thought that I was being menaced.

"He's a mighty queer dog, Miss," Frank said apologetically. "I never seen one like him in all my life——"

"He's a mighty fine dog too," my father broke in, "and we can't condemn him on this sort of evidence. Frank, I think you'd better clear up this mess while we think what's best to do—and you come with me," he added, looking at me.

Ajax and I followed my father. I couldn't speak, I was cold with fear and misery.

"Ajax *is* a strange dog, as Frank said—" my father put his hand on my shoulder—"and if he's turned killer you know that there is only one thing—a bullet. *You* know that, and that if we don't shoot him someone else will, when this gets about. It would be better for Ajax to be killed painlessly by someone who loves him, than to be shot at by some stranger and perhaps only wounded."

Still I couldn't speak. I knew that my father was right. After a while I managed to mumble, "Not yet! Not yet, *please!* You don't *know* that Ajax did it. You can't hurt him—he saved my life!"

"No, we don't know that he did it, but it looks bad for him. I promise you that we'll be quite sure before we do anything. We owe Ajax a very big debt for what he did for you, and you know that I won't forget that.

I only wish your mother wasn't away, but I don't want her to hurry back if we can help it," he added in a worried voice.

I was very unhappy, for I knew something that my father did not know. I knew that Ajax, who was generally so quiet beside my bed, had been restless for the last two nights, and that last night when I sat up to see what was the matter with my dog I found him standing like a statue beside my bed. I put my hand under his muzzle to rub it and felt something sticky. When I looked, there was blood on my hand. I thought then that Ajax must have been hunting as he often did—just that. It was not until morning that I learned, in terror and misery, what this hunting might have meant.

As I always did when I was in difficulties, I went to Lewis and we talked it over, but I did not tell even Lewis about the blood on Ajax's jaws the night before. Talking didn't help at all. We both knew that it boiled down to the question of whether Ajax was guilty or innocent. If he was guilty, he must die. The only alternative was to keep him tied up for life, and we both knew that was unthinkable; it would only inflict a slow death on the proud, fighting spirit.

I walked down to the river's edge and sat for a long time with my arms round my dog's neck, and I knew that he was trying to comfort me with his nearness. Algy, and even Ben, always knew when I was unhappy, and left their happy hunting along the banks and huddled close to me, so that we all sat together, a miserable little bunch, with a girl in the center. I think that never in my whole life have I suffered more deeply than I did then, as a child, with my heart full of terror for my dearly loved dog. I put my face against his strong golden neck and wept bitterly.

That night I didn't sleep at all, and I kept my hand hanging over the edge of my bed, touching Ajax. I was thankful when the night was over and Ajax was still safe. But the calves were safe too, so that really proved nothing.

A watch had been kept on the yards, and this was to go on until the moon waned in three or four nights. The watchers sat in the little cow shed where big cracks in the roughly timbered walls gave them a view of the yard, while they were invisible in the darkness within. A loaded rifle leaned against the wall.

The day dragged on, and I forced myself to lie awake and keep vigil on Ajax the next night. The third night, try as I would to rouse myself, in the end I fell asleep— and woke to the terror of knowing that Ajax was not there!

I jumped out of bed and scrambled into my sandals and warm dressing gown, and stole out of the house. Of course Algy and Ben tried to follow me, but I sent them back so firmly that they gazed at me in amazement as I shut the gate. Then I ran toward the yard as quickly as I could. The distance between the house and the milking shed was bathed in the ghostly light of the moon, silver-white and coldly horrible to me that night, and I've never liked moonlight very much since then. Once, far in the distance, I was sure I could see a big form loping toward the yards.

For a little while I could hear the dogs snuffling and whining at the gate behind me, and my feet crunched on the crisp, frosty grass as the blades poked through the open straps of my sandals, and my feet got wetter and colder as I ran on. Again I thought I saw Ajax circling the yards in the far distance.

I reached the fence and began creeping round the wooden railings toward the shed, which was between me and the huddled calves. The cold, platinum light of the moon gave me the sense of being quite alone in a vast, desolate world. Hugging the wooden walls of the shed, I crept softly to the door and *sssshed* at Lewis and my father before they could exclaim at my appearance.

Then followed what seemed like hours of waiting, but it probably was not more than half an hour. Outside the calves were restless, but kept tightly packed together. We three crouched in the little shed, and presently we heard the thud of running feet. There was the jarring sound of a heavy body on soft wood, and on top of the railings we saw a huge, honey-colored shape, its fiery gold bleached by the moonlight—Ajax!

My heart thudded and I felt sick. I wanted to call him but I did not dare. I knew that what had to be done *must* be done. Lewis picked up the rifle silently, and the wicked muzzle pointed through the crack. The calves milled and churned in their corner. I closed my eyes and I prayed very hard. Then I felt my father's hand on my shoulder and I opened my eyes.

The moonlight shone down on Ajax, an Ajax that I did not know. Gone was his proud and splendid bearing. His tongue lolled from his mouth as he moved toward the frightened calves with short mincing steps that had an indescribable evil about them.

Then I wondered if I was going mad, for at almost the same spot on the rails appeared another huge dog. Gaunt and golden, he hung there for a moment, streaked by the silver of the moonlight, and then dropped to the ground. The creeping dog turned, and they stood for a moment facing each other, and even the ground seemed to vibrate to the low, shuddering rumble of their growls, sounds that were infinitely more dangerous than the snarls and yelps of lesser dogs.

Then the first dog sprang like an overstretched spring, so swiftly that to my eyes he seemed just a blur of light. The other dog's shoulder opened in a great gash, and his blood was black in the moonlight. He whirled like light, and this time it was the first dog's shoulder that was gashed. Sometimes we could hear the clash of their teeth as a swift wolf slash missed its mark; at other times there was no sound, but another of those terrible gashes opened and blood flowed down.

I turned to Lewis and said despairingly, "Lewis, help Ajax!"

"Dear little girl, I can't. I don't know which dog *is* Ajax."

"If I call him?"

"No! No, you mustn't do that. If you distract his attention, he may be killed."

Both dogs were covered with wounds; then, suddenly, one huge body hurtled through the air. In a moment the other's teeth met in his opponent's throat, the great legs twitched, and then the dog lay still. The victorious fighter lifted his bleeding muzzle from his victim's throat and gave a deep, long wolf call of victory.

I couldn't stand it any longer, and I called, "Ajax!"

The dog's long, haunting cry broke, and he turned his head in a puzzled sort of way, almost as if he'd been asleep. I called again, and the bloodstained figure turned toward my voice, the rifle was lowered, and my dog Ajax lifted his caked muzzle to me to be caressed.

I insisted on going with the others to look at Ajax's dead enemy.

My father murmured, "It is impossible to tell them apart!"

Lewis examined the fallen yellow carcass closely, then he mentioned the dead pup we had found in the log before we got to Ajax, and said, "This must be the third pup. I expect it ran into the log last, and wriggled out again while Ajax was blocked in by the dead body of his brother."

"Then Ajax has killed his brother," I said sadly, for I could not help thinking what a wonderful dog some-one might have had if this one had been given the same chance as Ajax.

"They obviously belong to the same family," Lewis answered, "but this one ran wild while Ajax was tamed—sort of," he added, smiling down into Ajax's very untamed eyes.

"Circumstantial evidence very nearly did for you, old boy," my father said, putting his hand gently on Ajax's torn head. Then I told them about the blood under Ajax's jaw which I'd found after that first night, for now it was obvious that he'd been examining his brother's victims.

Ajax had lost a lot of blood and his wounds were stiffening, but he walked home beside me with his old, proud step, and allowed me to attend to the worst of his wounds without a whimper. Then, with my dog beside me, I climbed into bed and slept soundly for the first time in three nights.

# CHAPTER VII

# AJAX CATCHES A HORSE THIEF

SOON after this my mother managed to get a governess for me. Brownie was a darling, an Englishwoman who really loved my dogs almost as much as I did. My lessons were not very serious, only nine to twelve, and with frequent holidays, so I soon settled down and began to enjoy them.

Matilda, my kangaroo, had been christened from the song "Waltzing Matilda," for the rolled swag on a sundowner's back was called a Matilda. These men, whom we called swaggies, used to tramp through the Australian bush, taking jobs only when they needed money, and every station gave them a ration of foods, and these rations were very substantial ones with tea, sugar, flour and pounds of meat. This custom really began in the early pioneering days in Australia when hundreds of empty miles stretched between properties, with little traffic and less water, and these swagmen often died of hunger and thirst.

Many swaggies called at Gunyan, collected their rations, talked a while and then wandered off to the next station. They were not a bad lot, just restless men who loved to wander, but of course there was an occasional bad one who took his rations and then robbed the henhouse or garden. I remember only one real criminal, but he did not get away with it for long—thanks to Ajax and to Billy, an excellent native Aborigine tracker who lived near us.

One of my father's greatest interests was picnic racing, for which the horses came from the best bloodstock and were always ridden by amateurs. Every year we had two days' racing, a day of polo, tennis and dancing, and there was always a houseful of guests—I can remember as many as forty people in my home at these times. Of course there was great rivalry among the horse owners for the splendid prizes. My mother had a great deal of jewelry that my father's horses had won for her.

The horses were not raced until they were two-year-olds, and one year my father had a very successful bay mare called Frasca. We were very proud of her, and when all the excitement happened Frasca was being groomed for her second year of racing, with the big meeting in about three weeks' time.

I came home one evening, after the dogs and I had spent our afternoon by the river, and I saw my great friend Lewis standing talking to a stranger. He was a dilapidated creature, a real swaggie, and so I walked over because I liked them very much and loved their stories. I said, "Good evening," and the man grunted something and gave me a surly look. I did not like his face nor his grumpy voice, so I had turned to walk away when Ajax, growling in his throat, walked stiff-legged toward the man.

I realized that Ajax was frightening when you did not know him, so I stopped and said to the man, "Ajax won't hurt you—he always grumbles like that. Come on, Ajax."

The man turned toward Ajax, and with an ugly look on his face he said, "Too right he won't hurt me!" Then before I could answer he kicked out and caught Ajax in the ribs, a heavy, sickening kick.

I was so astounded that I stood for a second gaping, before I even felt furious. I think that Ajax was completely surprised too—in all his life no one had ever done such a thing before. So he hesitated an instant, and then, with his lips drawn back in his terrible fighter's grin and his teeth gleaming white in the dusk, he sprang straight at the man, who went over backward under the weight of the dog. For an instant I saw Ajax astride the man, his wolf's jaws holding the man's throat, and I saw, too, the terrified expression in the man's eyes. Then Lewis and I moved together, and with my arms round Ajax's neck we dragged him away.

The man got to his feet swearing at the dog. Ajax's

teeth had bruised his throat, but had not broken the skin. Lewis told him to shut up; he had brought it on himself—he was lucky that Ajax had not torn his throat out.

I was holding Ajax and trembling so much with rage that I could not control myself. "Get out! Get your rations and get away from here. How *dare* you touch my Ajax? Get out ... or ... or I'll sic him onto you!"

The man looked as if he would have liked to kill us all, but he was frightened, supposing that I could not hold Ajax—or that I did not want to.

Then I heard Lewis say, "Come on, I'll get your rations. Then get on your way—and don't you ever come back again."

They went into the storehouse. I was terribly upset and examined Ajax carefully. It had been a hard kick, but Ajax was tough and no bones were broken. I could only hold the great head in my hands to tell him how sorry I was. My mother often talked to me about Ajax; he was so big and strong and had all the instincts of his wild breed, and she told me that never in his life must he know anything but love and kindness. Up to then he never had, and I could not bear to think that he had been hurt so treacherously.

In the morning the man was gone—and so was my father's beautiful mare Frasca.

As in all pioneer countries, the stealing of any kind of

stock is a serious crime. Then, too, we loved Frasca, and she was a valuable thoroughbred and by far the finest of my father's horses. So Lewis set off upriver to find Billy. All natives are wonderful trackers by our standards—far better than any white man. They can follow a trail where ordinary sharp eyes cannot see the faintest mark. Soon Lewis came back with Billy, and we all went along to Frasca's empty stable. The man could easily be fifty miles away by night time. As I loved watching Billy track, my father said I could ride part of the way with them.

At the stables Ajax got very restless and cast about, growling in his throat. I thought he might mix up the tracks for Billy, but he said to leave him alone. My brother and I used to love to hide from Ajax, but he always found us very quickly, and then he would give me such a disapproving look, as much as to say, "Do stop trying these silly tricks on me."

So Billy thought Ajax might be useful to him. Billy tracked on foot, and like all Abos he could cover fifty or sixty miles at a tireless lope. He was a thin, wiry man, his face the mulberry black of the true Abo, with a flat nose and lank hair; he wore a torn old pair of trousers, and his callused, splay-toed feet were bare.

Algy and Ben were most aggrieved when I made them stay at home because I did not know how far I would be going. We saddled our horses and followed Billy. For once Ajax seemed to forget me. He sniffed and cast along the trail with a single-mindedness that made me sure he knew that it belonged to the man who had kicked him the evening before. I felt afraid of what he might do if he found the man first, and I told my father this. He said, "Let the dog alone—we'll keep up with him."

We cantered along and found Billy standing looking very puzzled at the river's edge. Water is one thing that stumps even a tracker—for a while. The man might have crossed, or he might have ridden along the edge in either direction.

Then we heard Ajax's deep voice somewhere up-river. So with Billy trotting along the edge we rode our horses up the bank and cantered along to find Ajax baying at us from a shallow, pebbled crossing. Even Billy could see nothing, but Ajax seemed so sure that we followed him across. And then began a game of hide-and-seek that went on for hours. Eventually we found that the man had doubled back toward the home-stead again, evidently thinking that this would stump us—he had probably reckoned without either Billy or Ajax. And then, about five miles from home, the trail led us toward a jumble of rocks called Mooroobie's Cave. *Mooroobie* is an Abo word for a death adder, that sleepy deadly adder that lives in rocky places. We often picnicked there, and there were no more adders than there were in any rocky spot.

The Mooroobie rocks differed from other outcrops, for on top of a rocky hillside there were huge oblong stones, not unlike the pillars at Stonehenge, and these were jumbled about, forming a shallow cave with a sort of rocky lintel across the front and a low wall of rocks hiding the cave.

I was tired. My father tried to send me home, but I would not leave Ajax. No one expected to catch up with the man that day, and so my father let me stay. Now he worried about me, because as we stopped in a clump of trees we saw a thin spiral of smoke going up from the top of the hillock, and we knew that it must be the thief. I got off my horse as my father, Billy, Lewis and one of the stockmen talked together. There was no sign of the mare, but we knew that the thief could have hidden her somewhere among the rocks.

The men all carried rifles, and with his on his arm my father walked out from the trees and went toward the rocks calling, "Hi! You! Come on, come out of there. I want to talk to you!"

There was no answer. My father called again, and when there was still no answer he aimed at the top of the rocks and the bullet chipped a bit off and went whining into the distance. That did it. From behind the rocks a man stood up, and the sun glinted along the barrel of his rifle. He shouted back that if they wanted him they would have to come and get him. My father kept on walking toward the rocks and a bullet tore up the earth at his feet. He stood still, leaning on his gun and talking to the man.

It was then, peering through the trees and feeling very frightened for my father, that I noticed that Ajax was not beside me. I was torn between anxiety for my father and worry over Ajax when Lewis touched my arm and pointed to the side of the rocks where the man stood shouting back at my father.

There I saw my dog, but he was not the dog I knew; this was an untamed hunter pursuing his enemy. Like a shadow he crept forward, absolutely soundless in spite of the loose stones. Then I saw the great body leap with a feathery lightness onto the rock we called the lintel. It was above the man's head, and about four feet behind him. For an instant Ajax crouched there, and I knew that my father must have been watching him, and that he had gone on talking purposely. Then, like an arc of golden light, Ajax sprang straight onto the man's back. He yelled with fear, the rifle clattered down the outer rocks, and man and dog disappeared behind the big front rock. There was a deathly, frightening silence.

Lewis tried to hold me, but I tore myself away and ran as fast as I could toward the rocks, while my father and the men raced behind me. I was filled with fear for Ajax. If he had killed the man, then he would have destroyed himself too. In an agony of terror I scram-

Ajax sprang straight on the man's back.

85

bled over the rocks, and because I was small and light and agile as a monkey, and because I knew every rock on the hillock, I was the first to reach the top.

There, stretched in front of the rock, was the same tableau I had seen the night before—the man on his back, surly-faced and frightened-eyed, and over him standing my dog, an ominous rumble in his great chest, his eyes full of wild light and his muzzle drawn back in his grinning, wolf's snarl.

It was all right—the man was alive! I stood there a moment, panting, afraid to call Ajax before the men arrived. As soon as they stepped onto the rock with their rifles ready, I put my hand on my dog's head. Still growling, he stepped backward off the man's body, and we could see that the thief was quite unhurt except for a few bruises.

After the man was tied up I searched for Frasca and found her tethered between two rocks halfway up the hill. I led her down and rode on ahead, keeping Ajax with me, and left the men to cope with the brutal horse thief, who was made to cover the five miles of rough ground on foot before being handed over to the police for trial.

# CHAPTER VIII

# BENNY IN THE LIMELIGHT

**B**ROWNIE, my governess, made a special pet of Benny—probably because he was so small. But after Ajax caught the horse thief he got a lot of attention he did not particularly want. Benny was very jealous, and I am sure he was delighted when his own adventures turned people's attention back to him again. Benny always wanted to do everything the "big boys" did, and he loved to go mustering with me.

In the ordinary work on a cattle station mustering means riding out perhaps twenty miles to collect the cattle together, perhaps for a cattle buyer. The cattle are mustered into what are called camps, flat pieces of ground inside a semicircle of fencing. Perhaps five hundred head are driven in here. Stockmen and dogs keep them from getting out at the open side, and the buyer rides in among them and points out which beasts he wants. Then a stockman rides into the herd and cuts out, or separates, the chosen beasts. These are driven a little way into the open, to form a smaller herd of their own, until they are all gathered together and driven off to their destination.

Cutting out is great fun. The stock horses push the chosen beasts with their shoulders, twisting and turning with them until finally they separate them from the rest of the herd. My fat bay pony Buck was quite good among the stock, until it grew hot and the milling cattle raised the dust. Then he would get very bored, and if I was unreasonable about resting when he felt like it, he would turn his head and nip me. This was easy to do, because until I was older I never rode in a saddle, and when Buck was in a nipping mood I had to scramble about his broad back to get out of reach of his nips— which really were a bit too much!

Dear old Algy was too big to follow and too big to carry for long rides, though Ajax was tireless, and Master Ben made a to-do if he was left at home, and always ended by galloping after me on his short legs, sniffing the hoof tracks like a bloodhound that by some enchantment had shrunk into a small, silky bundle. So the naughty little dog usually got his own way, and when he was tired he would perch in front of me on the saddle, yelping whenever he sighted a rabbit or a kangaroo rat hopping through the grass.

When I first graduated from Buck to my beautiful chestnut mare Belle, she made a great fuss when Ben was handed up to me. But she soon got used to him, and Master Ben fancied himself terrifically as a horseman, and used to sit with his front paws on the mare's neck and his little rump on the flat pommel that stock saddles have, his hind legs dangling on either side. It seems mean to add that I steadied him with my right hand all the time and it exasperated him very much!

Ajax, who used to make sorties through the long grass whenever he suspected anything would interest him, used to cover probably thirty miles or more, and when we got home he would fling himself down and go off to sleep. But Ben, who had spent more than half the time riding and was not a bit tired, used to show off, running about and playing with Algy and casting withering looks at the sleeping Ajax.

One day we rode home in the cool of the evening, almost too tired to enjoy the evening laughter of the kookaburras. These are the most fascinating birds, with big, fluffy heads, small bodies and wedge-shaped tails. They usually have a laughing match morning and evening, beginning with chuckling sounds and rising to shouts of laughter. This evening they were laughing all around us, and Ben, who was most exasperatingly lively, spied a rabbit and wriggled and struggled so that I thought, Very well, my boy, if you have all that energy just you go and chase your rabbit! So I slid him to the ground over my foot and off he went, *yap-yap* after the rabbit.

I was nearly asleep with tiredness when I looked around to see if Ben wanted to be picked up again, and he was not there. I called out to the stockmen riding ahead of me, and they told me not to worry, we were only walking our tired horses and Ben would be sure to catch us up. After another mile, and no sign of Ben, I felt too worried to go on and called to the men not to wait, as I was going back to call Ben.

We were only a mile or so from home, so I turned the tired, reluctant mare and called Ajax. We went back calling "Benny!" every few yards. He never came. It was getting very dark, for there is no twilight in Australia, and the dark comes like a swiftly dropped curtain. There was no moon, and the clear sky full of brilliant stars gave little light.

Finally there was nothing for it but to ride home. I was terribly worried, but I knew I must have light and help to search further if Ben, as I thought, was stuck in a hollow log.

I rode wearily home; my father said I must go to bed and at daylight we would all go to search for Ben. Dear old Algy kept running around and sniffing in the corners, obviously missing Benny very much, while the heartless Ajax went sound asleep. I thought that I would not sleep a wink, imagining my little fellow frightened and hungry, perhaps injured, but I was so tired that I did fall asleep very quickly.

At dawn I awoke, called my father and Lewis, and we caught and saddled the horses. As it was not far we decided to take Algy, feeling that the dogs had a much better chance of finding Ben than we had. We had an early breakfast and set off.

Usually I loved early-morning bush rides, but that morning I was too worried to enjoy the pale spears of sunlight like a flight of honey-golden arrows going away in the distance, as the sun swept up from below the horizon. Soon it was brazenly hot and the vivid blue of the skies pressed down on our heads. The mare jingled her bit and curtsied at her shadow, but I was too worried to enjoy it. We went slowly on account of Algy, but it was not long before we turned off the dusty road and the horses stepped delicately among fallen boughs and rabbit holes.

We spread out and called to Ben every little while, and the dogs ran and sniffed and toured in wide circles, but they had no luck. We went on searching until it was nearly noon and the heat was scorching, dry, Australian heat that seems to burn as you breathe it in, and then we turned sadly homeward. My father and Lewis tried to comfort me, saying that even now Ben might just turn up at the homestead. But I could not be comforted.

Even Ajax seemed worried, and he kept very close to me as he always did when he thought that I was unhappy, and did not growl when unhappy Algy tried to climb into my lap. Algy hung over my small lap every way, but he seemed to be soothed by the idea that he was a puppy again, so I put my arms round him to hold up the overlapping bits, and it seemed to comfort him as much as it comforted me.

That horrible day crawled by, and when it was a little cooler we went back to the place we had last seen Benny. This time we took the car and left it on the road while we walked slowly among stumps and trees and holes, but it was no use.

Next morning I got up before daylight, saddled my mare, and the dogs and I went back toward where we had last seen Ben, then turned and went up beside a fence for about a mile, for I decided to double back and comb the country toward the road instead of away from it. I had a water bottle on my saddle and gave the dogs a little, saving the rest for Ben—if we found him. I led Belle and walked in wide circles, calling, and examining every hole and rotted log on the way.

After a couple of hours of this I was very weary, my feet hurt and all my discouragement and misery rushed over me. I threw myself down in a piece of the sparse shade, turned on my face and cried miserably. Presently I felt Algy snuffling at me, licking my ear, snorting and nudging at me, and I thought he was just trying to comfort me. He kept it up, and presently I realized that all this business meant something. He trotted off a few steps, barking. I sat up; he was looking back at me and making the snorting noises he always did when he wanted me to follow him, so I got up and obliged. Then he seemed to lose his way, and rushed hither and thither, panting and blowing, and finally stood head down, yelping excitedly. I ran over to him, and he had his blunt nose stuck down the hole of a rabbit burrow. He sniffed and began to dig.

I bent down and called, "Ben! Ben!" There was no answer and I called again. I thought I heard an answering whine. It was only a tiny sound, but it *was* a sound—I was sure of it! I pushed Algy away and dug my hands into the earth. It was packed and hard. I tore my hands and broke my nails, but I could not dig it away. So I stood up and looked about for something with which to mark the spot. When I found a stick I tied my handkerchief to the top and dug it in the earth. Ajax was sniffing about the hole, but I would not let him dig because if the burrow were very honeycombed he might make the earth crash down onto Ben—if it was Ben!

Algy was a problem. If I left him he would be sure to dig, and if I took him with us he would slow us up so much. In the end I hurt his feelings by taking off a stirrup leather and tying him to a tree. I felt a brute, for he had never been tied up before, and he gazed sadly at me wondering what he had done to deserve this, while I jumped on the mare and tore for home in my stirrupless saddle. For once I let the mare gallop full out, but she never outdistanced Ajax, who loped easily beside me the whole way.

When I arrived home a stableboy took the mare, Lewis brought shovels, and I rushed to the kitchen and filled one bottle with milk and another with water, and we were ready. Ajax and I bundled into the car, Lewis drove, and we reached the spot in no time. Algy rushed about delightedly when I freed him, and as usual bore me no malice. I ran to where my handkerchief waved above the grass. I bent down and called to Ben, but there was no answer, and I was very afraid.

Lewis began digging carefully, following the winding burrow, but the ground was very hard and many passages led off from the main one. After about half an hour's hard digging we came to what seemed to be a fall of earth. We scraped this out with our hands, and there, behind the loose earth in a little pocket of space, was my Ben—not the lively bully we knew, but a weary, bedraggled little dog that for once wanted to be petted and made much of.

He was very weak—there had not been much air in the passageway—and he was very dirty. Algy was beside himself with delight and nuzzled and licked Benny joyously, and even Ajax unbent enough to come over and take a look at Ben to make sure he was all right. I carried the little dog to the car and gave him some milk and water. The little fellow was terribly thirsty. Then I dipped my handkerchief in the water and wiped some of the dust and caked dirt from around his eyes and jaws. He actually settled down on my knee in the car, and we stopped once to give him another drink.

I was so happy at having the little chap that I could

not speak. Poor Benny! What he must have suffered from heat and thirst imprisoned in that sun-baked earth no one knows. Probably this should have been a lesson to him against being so cocksure, but it was not. By the time we reached home, not half an hour after he'd been rescued, he was trying to struggle upright on my knee and to give a feeble ghost of his usual shrill yap when he sighted everyone lined up to welcome him! He really was very weak, and when I put him in his basket beside my bed he was quite happy to call it a day and to go straight off to sleep. Dusty and dirty as he was, I felt that a bath should wait until he was his arrogant self and could snap at the soap bubbles, scold me and squirm away, wet and slippery as an eel, to roll himself dry on the lawn.

CHAPTER IX

# BENNY TO THE RESCUE

OF COURSE Benny was outrageously spoiled after so nearly being lost for good, and one way and another he managed to keep himself in the limelight most of that summer—mainly because my brother and I taught Benny a trick since he was such a little show-off and enjoyed doing it so much. We would tie a message to his neck and tell him to carry it to one or the other of us, or to Lewis or my father, and very soon he learned to dash from one to the other feeling very important. In the end he would gallop half a mile on his fat little legs and deliver the message faithfully.

It was a dry summer, and the muddy river water lay as still as a lake beneath the low bank, and the water was almost too discolored to reflect the elegant trunks of the silver gums that grew behind the willow trees lining the banks. Their branches ended in a tangled growth on the surface of the water, and waterfowl would nest in them. I loved to watch the small black hens scurrying along half-submerged logs on tiny bright-red feet, or swimming near the bank, followed by the fluffy blobs of their waterwise brood. I would squat on a log and watch the chicks and the defiant water spiders skating round my finger tips, or peer into the bottle-green water, looking for the ghostly, transparent forms of fresh-water shrimps that I can see clinging to submerged logs, while above them the water closed sluggishly over the slimy satin ribbons of the waterweeds.

One morning the three dogs and I walked aimlessly along the riverbank until we came to a gully running inland from the water. I turned and walked up this, and ahead of me lay a coffee-colored cow, right in the hot noonday sun. It was Corabelle, one of the prettiest of the milking herd. She lay there motionless, except for the swaying of her head which gave the impression of distress and suffering.

I called, "Hullo, Corabelle!" and walked quietly toward her, telling the dogs to keep back. When I got near I could see that the great dark eyes in her swaying head were full of pain. So I squatted beside her and rubbed her chocolate-dark forehead, saying, "What's the matter, old girl?" There was no good shade near by, for the tall gum trees, with their pointed, gray-green leaves turned sideways to the sun, threw a mere dusting of shadowy confetti across the hard gold of the sunshine.

Something was very wrong with Corabelle; I rose to my feet and walked around her. Her creamy-coffee sides were pressed upward by the earth; her body trembled and quivered. I touched her side, and the burning heat of the sun and the animal heat of the hide together troubled my palm. I came round to her head, and then I saw her near foreleg.

"Oh, Cora! Poor Cora, you're hurt!" I cried, and squatted down again and passed my hand over her delicately carved, silken head in an effort to comfort her. I pulled off my old straw hat, but it looked small and silly between the cow's head and the sun, with all that great body burning and shuddering beyond it. Saliva dripped from the cow's mouth, and now and again she made a low mooing noise, full of sorrow. I put my hat on again and looked around for some way to shelter her. Even the dogs seemed to be feeling the heat, and lay panting in the sparse shade.

I knew that Corabelle must be dreadfully thirsty, and I walked back toward the river, looking for something in which I could carry water. There was nothing. Close to the water's edge someone had left a rusty old fruit can, but the cow could not get her muzzle into that. I dipped my hat into the water, but it simply poured through.

Then I had a bright idea—Ben should take a message back to Lewis! I tore a strip from the hem of my cotton frock and made some ink by puddling up a little water in the rusty can. On the material I scratched a shaky "SOS," and with another strip I tied the message round

Benny's neck, because, of course, the little dog could not run all that way without panting. He wriggled with eagerness, and I said, "Take it to *Lewis*—to *Lewis*," and off he galloped.

I was still puzzled how to get water to Corabelle when I stumbled across a patch of broad, green dock leaves growing from the brown leaf mold that edged the water, thickening every year when autumn came and the willows shed their leaves. I picked a big handful of dock leaves, and squatting on the leaf mold, I pushed the stems and leaf tips into the straw hat, and then added bits of the clay mud to make them stick down, twining leaves into all the crevices, until finally the crown of the hat had a thick, leafy lining. Then I gave it an experimental dip into the water. It leaked badly, of course, but if I carried the rusty fruit can full of water as well as the hat, it would give Cora a few cool sips.

I staggered up the bank, never raising my eyes from the diminishing water, and when I got to Corabelle the hat was still half full. I put it before her and stroked my wet hand across her muzzle, so that she would understand that this strange bucket held water. Cora put out her long tongue and drank thirstily. Then I jumped to my feet, meaning to refill the hat and the can. I heard Algy coming toward Cora and told him to go back. He gave a funny little whine and I looked up. Imagine my terrific excitement—for the first time I noticed that Cora had twisted herself into a half circle, and there, lying near her on the sunburned grass, small and wet and beautiful, lay a newborn calf!

It was a miracle of life, and I knelt before it and touched the little creature gently, while the helpless mother stirred her heavy body and tried to move nearer to her calf. I knew what she wanted and put my arms round the honey-colored mite and pushed it against its mother. The baby made a few weak little movements with its small head, dwarfed by the big ears of a baby animal, and looked at the world from great, liquid black eyes, then bent its head and started to drink.

I ran back to the river and brought more water, and when Cora had had enough I kept wetting her hot head with the cool water until I heard shouts in the distance. Then I stood up and ran up the bank, and there was my brave rescuer, Benny, galloping madly through the tall brown grass stems, with Lewis in hot pursuit, but still some way behind him. Benny sprang into my arms, thrilled with himself! He gasped and panted and his tongue hung out like a little piece of red flannel.

Lewis called, "What was the SOS about?"

"It's Cora. Oh, Lewis, I'm so glad you're here!"

Lewis went quietly to Cora's head and rubbed her ears. "Now, old girl, let's see that leg."

Poor Cora mooed unhappily.

One look told him the leg was broken. "We'll need help. We must build her a shelter here."

"And the baby calf?"

"That'll be up to you. You can bring it up on the bottle."

"Oh, I couldn't take it from Cora!"

Lewis looked worried. "She can't do much for it. She'll have to lie here until her leg sets and be fed and watered where she is."

"All right. I'll look after them both," I said.

Then Lewis took his big sheath knife and cut some forked branches, and rigged rather a shaky shelter over the cow and her calf. Then we went home to get splints for Cora's leg and other things. I was not allowed to return with the men, but Lewis said I could come along in an hour. When we got there Cora's leg, which had fortunately been broken low down, was set, and the shelter and fence were almost built. Cora had a heap of hay in front of her and water within reach; the ceaseless, suffering movement of her head had stopped, and she no longer moaned.

We lifted the baby onto its trembling little legs and for a few moments it stood looking at us with its great eyes. Then it folded up like some lovely velvet toy and lay close to its mother again. I knew that ordinarily Cora would lick her calf tidily all over and nudge it until it rose to its feet every now and again, so that it would soon be strong enough to get up and down easily. And Lewis told me that I must do Cora's work for her; get the calf up and down and rub it down every day with a soft rubber sponge squeezed out of salty water.

Finally we left them both well provided for, and Algy, Ben and I scrambled into the truck with the others, while Ajax loped alongside, and we all went home.

My father came home from his trip next day, and as I was with Cora he walked up to see me. He put his hand on my shoulder and said, "You're a good girl. But for you Cora would have died, so now it's only fair that she and her calf should belong to you."

I was very excited, but I said, "What about Benny? He did it really."

"It wouldn't be much use giving them to Benny!"

"Anyway, I think we ought to make a fuss of him——"

"All right, we'll do just that, though I can't think of any extra fuss we *can* make. We can't give him more pocket money!"

That night I was very happy as I lay in bed looking into the deep bush night that lay where the velvety-black stretched away from the veranda, and I thought of my beautiful cow and her calf. From the trees at the river's edge a hundred yards away came the soft *ka ka kakaka* of a possum; then the cry of a dingo, full of an infinite melancholy; and the sound I loved best of all, the sound that even now makes my heart turn over with homesickness, the surging sea-sound of a herd of calves penned into the yards and calling to their mothers outside, their cries rising and falling and filling the night air.

There was one more sound before I dropped off to sleep. Benny trotted to the veranda steps, and I saw his small back, black against the moonlight, as he raised his little nose high in the air and gave one long, quavering, miniature wolf call. Then he trotted back and jumped on my feet where he loved to sleep, and from where he took great pleasure in lording it over the other dogs.

CHAPTER X

# ALGY AND THE STONE
# AGE MEN

ALWAYS in the back of my mind ran the thought of the dread day when I would have to go to boarding school. Then, when Brownie came to us and I enjoyed my lessons so much, the fear of something that grew nearer year by year faded again. But just after Corabelle and her calf joined my own particular family, I overheard my mother and father and Brownie in a conversation that started me fretting once again over the thought of school and the leaving behind of all the creatures I loved. I found that my parents were very worried because I had no other children to play with. I did not consciously miss other children, but they thought it was bad for me to be brought up in this solitary fashion, and they were considering sending me off to boarding school instead of waiting until I was fifteen, as they had always meant to do. The thought of this seemed to bring the separation from my dear dogs very near to me.

I heard my father say, "The child simply adores the

new calf," and my mother answered, "I know, it does worry me. Every new animal means another tie for her to break when she goes to school, and she is going to be so dreadfully unhappy, I do feel that for her own sake we should send her soon now."

I could not listen any more. I called the dogs and we went wandering through the bush until I was very tired, and then we came home and I went silently to bed, refusing my tea, and my mother came to my bed and inquired anxiously if I were ill. I could not tell her what troubled me. Like all bush creatures I had learned to keep my fears to myself, and it was long after she left me that I went to sleep. Then, later that night, something happened that drove all thought of school out of everyone's minds for many months and gave us a new and wonderful experience, even though it was rather terrifying at the time.

Early in the morning hours I woke up to find the dogs whining and pawing at my bed. Smoke drifted through the night air, there was a great crackling noise, men shouted, and the tall gum trees along the riverbank were lighted by a brilliant, flickering light. Then my mother and one of the station hands came to my bed, rolled me in a blanket and carried me, still half asleep, off the veranda and away from the house, with the dogs running alongside.

Fire had broken out—one end of the long house was blazing, and the kitchen was already a mass of flames and charred wood. There was a stiff breeze blowing, and it was all the men could do to beat the flames back from the rest of the house.

The result of this fire was that after a lot of talking it was decided that my parents and I would go for the next few months to our other station, Gulaggi, which was on the fringe of the Central Australian desert, and that Brownie should have a long vacation. My mother and I had never been to Gulaggi. It had always been considered too primitive and too difficult a journey for us; but we both had always wanted to go, because around there was the really primitive life of Australia, and it was the last stronghold of the wild Myall natives.

This journey should have made both Ajax and Benny more humble, if they had only realized it. For Ajax, the kingly, aloof dog with the golden beauty of ripe corn, and Benny, the naughty little show-off, meant very little to the Myalls, who looked on Algy, humble, sweetly stupid Algy, as a god. The Myalls had never seen a bulldog before, and so he seemed a god to them. Ajax was a devil, and Benny, who considered himself a vastly superior type to the other two, was to the Myalls not even a very good snack, and I am sure he would have ended up in a cooking pot if I had not watched him every minute. He would have been so angry if he had known why the Myalls took the slightest interest in him!

My parents decided to make the long journey in the truck and to take the dogs as we always did. Much of the trip was through wild bush country, with tracks but no roads, and we had to take lots of spares for the cars, food and water, mosquito nets and goodness knows what else, for the journey took weeks.

Finally we started, and let the dogs out every few hours. They ran after the slowly moving truck, Algy puffing and blowing and getting picked up first, then Benny and lastly the tireless Ajax. During the last part of the trip we touched the fringe of the desert, where the air was so hot and dry that it burned and the vivid blue of the sky hurt the eyes. Around us grew the drab spinifex bushes, mulga, mallee and kurrajong trees. Once we passed what seemed to be miles of scarlet carpet, but which was really the beautiful, brilliant desert pea. Then we met our first camel train, twelve of the queer, awkward creatures, swaying along with their ungainly walk, prodded by their Afghan driver, snaking their long necks and grumbling and snarling bad-temperedly to themselves the whole time.

Insects and mosquitoes were very troublesome, and I wore long blue overalls. These later completely foxed the Aborigines, who never could decide whether I was a little girl in boys' pants, or a little boy with long hair!

We found Gulaggi homestead much smaller than Gunyan and with a mosquito-net-screened veranda running all around it. Central Australia is a strange, dry country. Where scattered showers fall, there may be patches of moist green grass, as well as flowering shrubs and bright quandong and acacia trees, but for the most part it looks, I think, rather like the lunar landscape will look to the first man who reaches the moon—a vast, strange land of subdued colors, dry and crumbling. Here and there are small hidden water holes, or the dry shine of salt-encrusted lakes, and endless plains out of which great rocky formations rise abruptly, like colossal natural cathedrals with rounded roofs.

In this sparse and rather terrible land live the scattered tribes of Aborigines, usually called Myalls, I suppose from the skimpy scrubs that give them shelter. These stringy, muscular warriors hunt with spears of their own make, and they are so black that they have the purplish tinge of a mulberry. They wander about the trackless land, forever searching for food, eating anything they can capture or spear—iguanas, birds, desert rats, emus, wild camels—or digging the yams which grow in patches in the hard earth and which taste like sweet potatoes. They live just as their ancestors lived, the Stone Age men of countless thousands of years ago. For water they have only their soaks, muddy little water holes which they keep carefully hidden and which have been known to their tribes from time immemorial. These soaks mean life itself to the natives, who often travel a hundred miles between them in their never-ending search for food.

It was probably the travelers' tales told so often to my father that decided him to make a trip south to see the amazing Ayers Rock, which rises straight from the plains to a height of a thousand feet and is about two miles long and a mile broad. My mother did not want to go on the long and difficult trip, but my father agreed to take me and, of course, the dogs.

Jim, an old bushman near us who had been in this land for forty years and could talk to the Abos, decided to join us. He was a great friend of mine, and knew a great deal about this strange life around us. Jim had a wonderful collection of the Abos' work—their canoe-shaped wooden pitchis, in which they carry food; their spears and womeras, the sticks which they use for launching their spears; and he even had a pair of the rare *kaditcha* shoes, which are worn only by medicine men and are very sacred. They are made of emu feathers stuck together with human blood, and even the miraculous native trackers cannot tell which way a man is walking when he has them on. The Abos say that when a man wears the *kaditcha* shoes he becomes endowed with supernatural powers.

I was delighted that Jim was to be in our party; he loved the dogs and they loved him, so of course he could

do no wrong in my eyes. The first day of the trip we
had two punctures, but these things came as a matter of
course; the heat and the dry, thorny things that come
out of spinifex are very hard on tires.

We often saw willy-willys circling about the endless
bare lands. A willy-willy is a sort of whirlwind that
looks like a thin brown column of smoke dancing across
the plain. When one is near you it looks like a spinning
cone, its center a vortex of wind and sand and anything
else the willy-willy picks up on its mad journey. We
were having our lunch one day, sitting on the side of the
truck in the shade, when a willy-willy raced toward us,
and before we could scramble out of the way it hit us!
It whirled Ben several yards away and filled our food
with sand. It took us about an hour to collect our scattered utensils and to get what sand we could out of our
clothes and Ben's coat. Benny was most indignant
about the whole thing. I am sure he thought it was a
silly trick we had played on him, and he snarled and
grumbled for ages after the willy-willy was far away.

Now and again we would see about a dozen desert
men standing on hilltops, or peering from among the
dried grasses of the plain, their lubras, which is what
they call their women, standing behind them carrying
the tiny children who were too small to walk, or else
holding their fire sticks—long pliant branches bound
together at the top, decorated by knobs of brilliant red
from the shiny seeds of some desert plant. The naked

ildren peered through matted hair decorated by a sort
shaggy fringe that went all around the head,
eighted down by brown seed pods about as big as
rapes.

The dogs were always restless when the Abos were
bout, and I used to keep them close to me, especially
en, after Jim warned me that the Abos would love to
it him! Sometimes we saw native children with the
iost extraordinarily distended tummies, and Jim said
iis was because they, like the camels, filled themselves
p at water holes, drinking until they could hold no
iore, because the water had to last them until they
eached the next hole.

One day I found Algy almost standing on his head,
s he did when he wanted to sniff at anything on the
round, so I looked and found he was peering at a fat,
egless, ant creature. I scooped it up on a piece of bark
nd took it back to Jim, who told me it was a parasite
nt, one of a tribe of desert ants with the unpleasant
iabit of biting the legs off a few of their brothers. They
hen stuffed the helpless ants with food until they got
olling fat; then during the hard winter the rest of the
ints ate those living storehouses.

Later on Algy and Ben were both delighted with
hemselves when they dug out another sort of these
annibal ants. These were called honey ants, and they
stuffed members of their tribe with honey as reservoirs
for hard times. The dogs found the fat, helpless,

honey-filled creatures delicious, but I must say thought it revolting of them.

One day Jim talked with a desert warrior he knew a big, gaunt man with a plait of grass round his forehead to tie his shaggy hair back and carrying a narrow wooden shield and a long barbed spear. Jim learned that the tribe was having a corroboree that night on sacred ground not far from our camp. The warrior chief agreed that we might see it, on condition that we kept very quiet, the dogs were left behind and the "boy"—that was I—kept quiet and stood behind the two men.

When the moon rose we shut our dogs in the back of the car and walked quietly to a little rise overlooking the ground, where we were almost hidden by grass and bushes. We could hear the Abos before we reached the rise, making strange, savage, chanting noises, and when we were in sight it was a savage picture too. The Myalls, their bodies shining with grease and banded in ocher and white, were rattling their spears and womeras and stamping their feet in savage rhythm. They had bunches of dried grass thrust through their nostrils, like mustaches that were growing too high up, and round their heads were strips of furry hide and grass to hold back their wild, matted locks.

I watched entranced. No women were allowed on the sacred corroboree grounds, and the lubras squatted in the background, nursing their children and keeping their backs to the dancing warriors. After a time the painted, weaving bodies, the steady stamping and hoarse cries seemed to mesmerize me, and the next thing I knew was that Jim was carrying me back to the car!

"You're a fine one to fall asleep when I take you to a party!" He laughed, and I *was* annoyed with myself. I knew I would probably never see another corroboree just like that one—and I never have.

We were about a day away from Ayres Rock, with the dogs out of the car and having a run, when we heard the rare sound of Ajax's deep bark. My father stopped the car and we went toward the sound. Ajax was standing over the figure of a man, an Abo lying in the dry grass. Jim rolled him over. He was an old man, and unconscious.

"Thirst," Jim said, and put his finger into the man's mouth and hooked out a stone. The natives carry stones in their mouths to help them keep down their thirst. The men carried the old fellow back to the car and gave him a little water, and presently he came to, and Jim told him that Ajax had found him. With the great toughness of these Stone Age men he soon recovered and was as good as new. It seemed he had some sort of accident, and, as they always must, the tribe, which was on a migration from one soak to another, had left him.

The old chap was delighted with the food and drink

we gave him, and seemed most grateful in his own way. We put down a piece of tarpaulin for him to sleep on, but in the morning he was gone.

The next morning, in the dawn sunlight before us, the great Ayers Rock rose like a tower of shimmering gold. No wonder it was a sort of sacred temple to the Abos, who knew all the huge, red-walled caverns high up its sides, on the walls of which their ancestors had drawn bats and birds, and strange, ghostly figures.

On the horizon was the thin, wavering spire of bluish "talk" smoke, for the Abo, like the Indian, uses colored smoke made by different plants to talk from one tribe to another. We were to camp near a water hole at one end of the Rock. Around the hole the skimpy trees were filled with small, screeching parrots and a species of doves with plumage of softest blue. And there, standing beside the water hole, was a baby emu, the dearest little thing with a three-cornered face and wearing what looked like a jumper of brown and black stripes. It was not a bit afraid, and Algy and I wanted to adopt it, but Jim said it would be better back with its mother, and presently it wandered on.

Just as we pulled up another tire went, and while the men were working on it the dogs and I started up the face of the Rock. It was terribly hot, but I climbed on and on, with the dogs struggling and panting beside me. Presently we landed in one of the big, bare caves that honeycomb the Rock. Ajax loped out of sight through the open end of the cave, and suddenly I felt far away from everyone and rather frightened. I told myself not to be silly, and that it would be stupid to go back without exploring. Ben was still with me, but Algy had disappeared. I called; the echoes came back to me but not the dogs. Then Ben gave a yap and pelted off to the end of the cave and disappeared. I waited awhile, calling him and looking at the scrawled drawings on the walls.

Then I got panicky and ran to where the dogs had disappeared. I found myself in a boulder-strewn passage which was very dark. I felt my way along, and then suddenly my foot slipped on the loose stones and I felt myself falling, clawing and scrabbling at the loose rocks and sand that fell with me. I must have fallen fifteen feet or more when I came to a slithering stop and stood up. I looked around me, and I knew real terror!

I was in a great, red-walled cave. All around the walls were scrawled aboriginal drawings—men and beasts made from single strokes of some sort of ocher-and-brown pigment. Then I heard Ben's familiar yap, and I looked across the cave to where, still and silent, a dozen gaunt, wild-looking warriors stood.

In the center of them was Algy, panting heavily and looking very bewildered and embarrassed. Round his neck was a noose of plaited grass. In front of him squatted an evil figure that I knew must be the medicine man, for at his side was the little dilly bag, or leather pouch, in which medicine men keep such "sacred" objects as bits of human bone, strands of hair, dried lizards and so forth. In front of him lay Ben—Ben with his little legs tied together with grass rope, his red tongue panting, and every now and again yelping with indignation. Around this group was drawn a circular line of white. I remembered what Jim had said about Benny making a nice titbit for an Abo's supper!

Algy tried to come to me. He wriggled and twisted and the grass noose tightened, but it would not give. The warriors stopped moving about and stood absolutely still, obviously taken aback by my sudden entrance. I moved toward the group, and two of the warriors stepped between me and the dogs and stood immovable. I could only think of one thing to do, so I raised my voice and called despairingly, "Ajax! Ajax!"

For an instant everything was still; then there was a rush of feet and Ajax bounded through the opening behind the warriors, leaped across Algy and reached my side, turning to face the men, his hackles erect, his eyes a warning red, and that terrible, slow thunder vibrating in his chest.

The medicine man scrambled back from Ben, who yelped and struggled harder than ever, and Algy stood still and gazed beseechingly at Ajax and me. I put my hand on Ajax's shoulder, and, stiff-legged and menacing, he stepped forward, while I tried not to look frightened and shivered with terror inside. Again we moved a step forward, and I thought that the warriors did not look quite so confident. Certainly the medicine man was upset; he scrabbled about in the dust of the ring gabbling to himself. We moved forward again— and through the opening ahead of us came another black figure.

There was something familiar about this man, but I was not sure what it was. He stepped forward and squatted down in the circle, facing the first medicine man, and the newcomer threw his dilly bag down by his side. It was clear that the first man just did not know what to do; and the warriors, instead of standing with that dreadful stillness, began to move and mutter among themselves. Ben had stopped yapping; he just whimpered a little, which broke my heart, but I dared not move toward him until I was sure what the new man was up to. There was much talk and shouting. Then the second man's voice rose angrily; the first man threw his arm across his eyes and scurried backward like some great black crab, and when he was outside the white circle he rose to his feet and ran through the gap in the wall.

The second medicine man rose to his feet and beckoned to me. I was still afraid, but I knew that I must not show it, and Ajax and I walked forward together.

Then I knew who the man was! He was the Abo we had rescued two nights before. I called out to him and he smiled and nodded his head. The rest of the warriors simply melted away through the dark hole at the back of the cave. I ran forward and untied Algy and Benny, and hugged them with relief and happiness. Finally the old man led the way down the cliffside, and we arrived back at the car, and I told my father what had happened, and the old man talked to Jim.

I went over to them and thanked him for saving us. We gave him some cans out of our food store, but this did not seem enough for all he had done for me, so I took off the gold bangle I always wore and gave it to him, because it was the best thing I had. He seemed very pleased, and I knew it would be a strong "medicine" with the tribe; then he walked away round the Rock.

Jim said that the warriors I had seen in the cave had followed us across country, using their own short cuts, because they had never seen any dog like Algy, and if they had been able to they would have kidnapped him long before because they believed he must be a very powerful god. But they were afraid of Ajax; they believed *he* was a demon. When they caught silly, friendly old Algy in the cave and trapped Ben, they did not anticipate that I would fall in from the roof. If I had not come along they would have sacrificed Ben to Algy!

But I appeared and called up the demon Ajax, and that made them doubt the power of their medicine man.

Even so, it might have ended tragically if the Myall we had rescued had not in his turn rescued us. Having met the great god Algy socially, so to speak, as well as the demon Ajax, who had saved his life, he felt he owed us all something, and he certainly more than paid his debt.

CHAPTER XI

# THE CAVE DIGGERS

WHEN we returned to Gulaggi from Ayers Rock, we had another two months to stay before it was arranged that we should return to Gunyan in time for my brother's long Christmas vacation. Although the fire had put off talk about my going to boarding school, I had a nasty feeling that it would be revived once I was home again. However, when we returned to Gunyan in due time and found Brownie waiting for us, I forgot my worry in the joy of playing with Matilda and the excited, loving welcome of Kiko and Possy. And then my brother arrived and he and I were together most of the time, riding, playing tennis and fishing through the long summer days.

One day we decided to dig a cave in the side of one of the few high banks that faced the river where it curved round the house. My brother liked to do things in a big way, so we set to work digging with a perfect fury that seemed to infect the dogs, and they began to dig furiously too—for a few minutes, until they got tired of the idea! Benny was always scrambling

120

The dogs began to dig furiously also.

121

through our legs and putting in his two cents' worth, which really was not much help from such a little fellow. But Ajax scooped out quite a lot of damp earth with his huge paws, and we would sit back on our heels and let him go at it. Algy could have been quite useful too, but he would dig for a moment, and then be so fascinated by the things he turned up—the wood beetles and earthworms and other wriggly creatures that love wet earth—that he would stop digging and begin to sniff and snuff whatever was wriggling about, snorting and barking when it tickled his nose. He would never have gone very far as a miner, I am afraid!

We were so pleased with what we were doing that we often stayed the whole day on the riverbank, taking a picnic lunch and splashing about in the cool water when we got too hot for words. When we were asked what we were doing, we simply said "digging a cave," and nobody bothered any more.

When we were very tired we would scramble down the bank and sit by a submerged log watching for the pale, ghostly shrimps to come walking along it on their threadlike legs. We collected some planks from Lewis and used them to shore up the crumbling sides of the cave, making rather a wobbly job of it. One day my father came down as we threw tea into the boiling water in an open billy can. We invited him to climb up the bank and take a look at our cave, but he only laughed and refused. Obviously he thought we had some tiny hole in the bank, and my brother and I looked at each other and did not say any more, making up our minds that as soon as it was big enough we would invite both parents to tea *in* the cave!

So we went on digging and battering planks into position, in between swims in which the dogs joined. One day Algy was paddling and snorting about the edge of the water when he yelped suddenly. We rushed toward him, he threw his head up, and to our horror something long and leathery and black was attached to the roll of flesh just behind the black button of his nose. The poor old boy was terrified, and so were we. He dashed about shaking his head, the thing clung on, and then we realized that it was not a snake but a big black horse leech—a horrid creature but not dangerous.

Algy calmed down after a bit, for leeches do not hurt at all, and when nothing worse happened than the flapping of the nasty thing about his face, he squatted on his haunches, shook his head and tried to peer at it, first with one eye and then with the other. All the time the leech grew fatter, until at last it simply dropped off. Then Algy bounded backward as it lay there on the sand, gorged and horrible but quite harmless. Algy gave a few snorts and half-hearted grabs at it until Benny noticed him. Then Benny, behaving like a Lord Mayor who is keeping a procession waiting, bounced up barking loudly, seized the thing in his little jaws and flung it into the air. Finally he flung it into the water and the portly leech floated away. Then you could almost see Benny dusting the palms of his front paws and saying, "There! *I* fixed that!" as he trotted away on some other all-important business that needed his attention.

As we dug deeper into the bank the work went more slowly. We stamped all the earth we had dug out into quite a little platform outside the cave entrance. Then we decided that we couldn't wait for the day when we would have the cave eight feet into the bank and five feet high, but, as we were halfway, we would give a preliminary housewarming.

So we gave up work for that day and went down on the beach and built a "volcano." The volcano was a big mound of earth and sand, damped and patted down until it was very firm. Then, as gently as possible, we tunneled from opposite sides—and the dogs were not allowed to help! When the tunnel was through and the center widened a little, we ran a straight, pointed stick from the peaked top to the lower chamber. This was the tricky part, for the whole thing might collapse. Once safely through this, it was time to search for kindling, tiny bits of dry wood or anything else that would make a good smoke. This was worked carefully into the middle hollow, and we lighted it with the blazing end of a dry stick. When the kindling caught, the smoke poured out of the hole at the top, and we sat around feeding the internal fires with tiny twigs—until we got tired of it.

We issued formal invitations to our parents, Brownie and Lewis for one Saturday afternoon, and with much heaving and pushing we managed to get quite a thick log into position on the platform outside the cave, as we knew that grownups did not think highly of sitting on the ground. We nailed slats across an old garden stool to make a table and put scraps of carpet on the damp floor. A small wooden box held the teacups, and I put a mass of wattle blossom into cans and jars inside the cave. This made both of us and the dogs sneeze violently. Benny went further than sneezing; he shoved his curious little nose into a thick clump of the golden blossoms and got stung on the tip of it by a bee that had refused to pick up its pollen knickers and fly away!

It was a hot afternoon as we waited for our guests, and we looked longingly where the river sparkled like silver paper in the sunlight and lay cool as gray glass in the shade of the willows. Benny had a blue bow round his neck, which he rather enjoyed, and he galloped down the bank and took an admiring peek at himself in the still, willow-fringed pools every once in a while.

Everything was ready, billy can boiling, sticky cakes wheedled out of the cook and covered by a tin plate to keep the flies off, when our guests arrived, hot and panting from their scramble up the steep bank. I thought my mother and Brownie behaved in the way guests should, but my father and Lewis behaved rather strangely as we gestured proudly toward the cave and they saw it for the first time. Feeling that they were not so impressed as they should have been, we hastened to explain that it was only half finished, and that we were going to dig at least twice as far into the bank before we stopped—then maybe we would camp right *in* the cave for the rest of the vacation!

Our father remarked feebly that we must have worked very hard. Lewis doubled his six feet into half and went into the cave and examined the shoring-up boards, then came out and said defensively, "I gave them the boards, Boss, but I didn't know they wanted them for *this!*"

"But we told you we were building a cave," I said. We were a little disappointed at the lack of enthusiasm, but put it down to the silly way grownups often went on. Then we ate a whopping tea ourselves, saw our guests off, tidied up and had a swim before we went home.

When we were in bed on the mosquito-netted veranda, our father came to say good night. He looked a little upset, and we soon found out why.

"I blame myself for not looking at the cave when you invited me, but—well, you know how busy I am. I had no idea your cave was in the curve of the bank that guides the water away from the homestead, nor that it was so big. It would be very dangerous to have that great hole there in flood time, so I'll have to disappoint you and ask you not to go on with the digging——"

At this stage I burst into loud wailings; now my brother would treat me like a baby again and I just could not bear it! At my wails the three dogs leaped onto the bed, or rather Benny and Algy did, nearly smothering me with their loving kisses, while Ajax stood with his front feet on the bed, towering over me, anxious-eyed and loving, growling at the invisible enemy he thought must be menacing me.

When everyone had calmed down a little, we both realized that our father was right. We just had not thought about the terrible floods that occasionally swept down on the homestead, like the one in which I had found Ajax. Next day Lewis examined the planks supporting the cave and said that we must not go in it again, because it might collapse any minute.

So we were forbidden our cave, and it was left for the planks to be removed and the earth to be filled in some time when there were men to spare for the job. But on a station there never *are* men to spare for anything, and so the cave stayed as it was.

When my brother went back to school I missed him dreadfully. It had been lovely to have my own brother to play with, and I tried hard to keep up with his much more grownup idea of games, taking all sorts of risks and being frightened to death half the time by the things he expected me to be able to do.

Then one day after he had returned to school I suddenly felt very lonely for him, and thought I would just *look* at the cave again and remember the happy time we had had digging it. Of course I would not go in—I would just *look*. So the dogs and I scrambled up the familiar bank and found the cave looking much the same, only rather dilapidated where there had been little falls of earth, or where the planks had buckled out from the sides. Then I felt I *must* crawl into it, just once, for old times' sake; so in I went with Benny in front, Algy just behind me and Ajax standing in the entrance. We three rather crowded it, and we bumped against the boards as we got to the end and were turning round to get out again.

Then it happened. Suddenly a shower of earth fell on us all. Benny turned and bolted out, but Algy was bigger and slower. I tried to hurry him out, for I was covered in a film of earth and half blinded by it and really terrified by the creaking, buckling noises from the wooden supports. In my fluster I noticed that Algy's hindquarters were in front of me as I turned toward the opening, and that I couldn't see his big head and shoulders, and there was only a gap of less than eighteen inches facing me. I got down on my stomach and wriggled through this, and then to my horror I saw that the wooden props had fallen across Algy's shoulders, and earth from the top of the cave had fallen too so that Algy was pinned there. Only his strong front legs allowed him to keep the space free for me to crawl through, and now that I was beyond him I could see his distress. He was panting and could not move; if his front legs gave way and released more debris, he would be crushed.

I did not know what to do, for I could see that he could not stand the pressure on his back for long. I tried frantically to find something with which to lever the load up, but there was nothing. In despair I stood for an instant trying to think of something, and then I heard the sound of horses' hoofs on the shingle of the river crossing below us. I turned toward the sound and saw two of the stockmen riding toward me, the reins loose on the necks of their tired horses. I stood still and screamed, "Help! Help!"

The men looked up and saw me. I yelled again, and they came galloping toward me, splashing through the shallow, glittering water of the ford. By now I was yelling and sobbing together. "Hurry—oh, do hurry! It's Algy. Oh, hurry, help him!"

They jumped off their horses and came scrambling up the bank, and I pushed them toward the mouth of the cave. They could see in an instant what was happening to my Algy, and they rolled the stump we had put outside for a seat right into the gap beside Algy;

then they managed to get a board from the mouth of the cave and to lever up the mass of earth and boards off Algy's back. Poor fellow! He staggered out panting, his legs trembling, and threw himself down outside.

"Phew! That was a near thing!" one of the men said. "Let the old chap rest a minute, then we'll take you home."

The men squatted on their heels and lighted cigarettes, and when Algy had recovered we all went home. I would have felt happier about this adventure if my father had insisted on a definite punishment for my disobedience, but he did not.

Had he known it, he did something far worse; he looked at my mother in a worried way and said, "That settles it, Jean. That child is like a wild animal, and she's always in danger of one sort or the other. She should be living like any other little girl, playing with children of her own age at *safe* games. Don't you see? She really should go to boarding school. Do make up your mind to it and get her ready to go to Armidale after the midwinter term."

That was punishment indeed.

# CHAPTER XII

# HOMEMADE CIRCUS

BIRTHDAYS were great events in our family, and because my brother's birthday fell on a day of his Easter vacation it was arranged that he should come home, instead of staying somewhere near the school as he usually did, except for the long, twice-yearly vacations when he always came home.

Actually his birthday fell on the day before he had to leave on his return to school, but that gave us nearly two weeks in which to plan some sort of party. The day after he reached home we walked up to the big round yard together. It was about a quarter of a mile from the homestead, and in the yard, which was shaded by a couple of rough-barked wild apple trees, lived a great Clydesdale stallion. Its huge hoofs were topped from knee to fetlock in what looked like ballet skirts of long hair, and its mane tossed from side to side from the fleshy crest that rose in a proud curve on the massive neck—it was a wonderful creature that looked as if it should be carrying a knight heavy with shining armor and a long jousting pole, such as only a powerful man on a giant horse could carry.

131

We watched the big draft horse thunder about the yards from where we perched on the top rail of the fence, and then the dogs followed us up a short ladder to the loft of the little building belonging to the yard, and the hay made us a comfortable couch. The dogs climbed ladders as well as we did, and Benny was a great tree climber and used to follow us up sloping trunks and along the lower branches, more like a cat than a little dog.

We lay there, panting with heat. The wooden doors left at least a twelve-foot gap where they were pushed back for greater coolness, and we watched the heavy stallion kick and squeal as a horsefly bit him on the rump.

We laughed, and Garth said, "It's just like a seat at the circus, sitting here and watching old Magnificence the Third kicking up his heels. . . . I say! How about a circus for my birthday?"

"Oh, *yes!* But how—?"

"It'd be easy. Lewis'd help, one of us could be ring-master while the other performed, and look—" he jumped to his feet—"we'd push the hay back and put a bench up here for the audience. *You* ought to be pretty good. Think of the circus performance you and the dogs gave at the Inverell Show last year!"

This really wasn't fair—it was not my fault that the dogs went on as they did. I had been upset at the time, but now I could laugh at it with my brother, as we looked back on it and planned our own circus.

That dreadful Inverell Show fiasco had happened because my father felt that my beautiful mare Belle was ready for the show ring. She was under fourteen hands high, which is the right height for a polo pony, and she was a bright chestnut with tiny brown flecks that could only be seen when her hide was rubbed upward. I was proud of those flecks because they were said to belong only to descendants of the great horse Carbine, and his stock was coveted by all horse lovers.

We always stayed with friends, the Andersens, in Inverell, because they had a big garden and loved to have the dogs. When we arrived for the show I was rather upset, because the Andersens, thinking it would be a nice surprise for me, had entered Algy in the show where his rivals were limited to one local bulldog! I would never enter any of the dogs in shows because I knew that they would hate it, but I felt I could not hurt the Andersens' feelings by refusing to show Algy, so I just made up my mind to make the whole thing as easy and pleasant for him as I could manage. None of my dogs were fit to be show dogs; they had never been tied up, or had even worn collars. Ajax would stalk at heel anywhere, but Algy and Benny simply had not a clue on how to behave in the street.

We went to the show ground and inspected the dogs'

pavilion, which was very nice, fitted with rows of wooden kennels, each one a gaily painted little house with a peaked roof, open in front and with a chain attached to the side of the door. We met an official who was most interested in Ajax; indeed, wherever I went people stared at him. I told the official how it came about that I was showing Algy, and he was most sympathetic and said I could tie Benny up with Algy and put Ajax in the kennel next door, so that Algy would have his own friends with him.

When the opening day arrived I was so upset about leaving Algy that I lost interest in my own events. I got into my riding clothes, and then we took the dogs to the show ring. I made a big sacrifice to soften Algy's hard lot and wrapped my party dress in a piece of paper and took it with us. It was a sapphire-blue velveteen, and Algy loved rubbing his face on it, so I thought it would comfort him to have it in his kennel, and I spread it well inside on the clean dry straw.

That evening my mother was amazed that she had left my frock behind, and sure that she remembered packing it!

The first day passed uneventfully, and Belle won the first heat for the best polo pony and came third in the ladies' hacks. My mother stayed with the dogs while I was in the ring, but I was with them the rest of the time, and Benny got very tired of being carried about because whenever I put him down he got into some trouble or other. Algy's rival was a fine, fawn-colored bulldog, used to shows and to being handled by strangers and to being tied up. It was absurd to pit my old fellow against him. Dear Algy! He had not a notion of how to behave while he was being judged, and wagged his tail, sat down and tried to lick the judge's hands all the time, so of course he did *not* win the prize. But as he was the only other bulldog entered they had to give him the second prize!  •

When the judging was over I patted Algy, told him how clever he was and tied Benny beside him, had a word with Ajax next door and rushed off to the ring to ride Belle in the polo-pony finals. That was the first time all three dogs had been tied and left without any of their friends near them. Opposite Algy sat his rival, handsome in his blue ribbon. Algy hated *his* ribbon, so I tied it to his peaked roof.

Belle won the first prize in her class, and I hurried back to collect the boys. As I neared the pavilion I heard the most awful row going on, and a crowd milled about outside. I wormed my way in, deafened by those frightful snarling, roaring savage sounds with which dogs always fight. I knew without looking that Algy's weakness for a fight had been too much for him, but I was not prepared for the sight that greeted me. Inside the hall I found the crowd pressed back against the wall, and in the center it looked as if several giant tortoises with brightly painted peaked shells had gone mad and were charging at one another, making fearful wooden bangings and splintering sounds to add to the noise of the dogs.

Algy had suddenly decided that he hated his rival just about at the moment his rival had come to the same conclusion, and they charged across the floor dragging their houses after them. Ben, bursting with excitement and chained to Algy's house, was dragged along too and added to the confusion by nipping both dogs, although I am sure he thought he was helping Algy. And he bounced backward and forward, trying to avoid having the kennel dragged over him!

At first Ajax looked on in his lordly way, but when officials rushed forward and tried to separate the dogs Ajax decided this move was directed against Algy, and he gave one of his great roars and dragged *his* house into the skirmish, chasing the officials and everyone else back against the walls.

There he was when I came in, raging backward and forward, his house bumping madly after him like a cockleshell, while behind him Algy and the blue-ribbon boy fought it out, tangling their chains, stamping on Benny and pulling their houses on top of themselves. Fortunately the chains held, so when I called Ajax to me and slipped his collar off, the officials caught hold of the other houses and parted the dogs by sheer weight.

What a mess they were, panting and snarling and bitten all over, but not deeply. The champion's ribbon was just a mess—and my velveteen dress . . . ! Algy's red ribbon still waved gaily from the peak of his house. I got Benny undone; he was unhurt but filthy, covered in the big dogs' slather. The owner of the champion was as worried as I was and kept apologizing to me. I was pretty sure that I should have been apologizing for Algy, but the mischief was done, so I let him take what credit he could for being the attacked and not the attacking one.

This was what my brother meant when he teased me about my circus act, but I told him he could not expect the dogs and me to do anything so spectacular as our show act over again. We decided to ask our father if we could move the stallion somewhere else for the time we needed to prepare the ring, and Mother said we could have the birthday party in the room below the loft. Then we went into a huddle and thought out the acts. Of course Algy, Benny, Ajax, Matilda and Kiko had to be in it, but we let Possy off because he was always so sleepy in the daytime. Then there were Buck, my fat pony, Lewis' cattle dog and my carpet snake Kaa. Kaa was beautifully marked and about nine feet long. He lived in a hole under the meat house and kept the rats away. He was a fat, gentle creature and seemed to like my pulling him about.

Then my brother did something that nearly wrecked the circus. My parents had a friend, a very nervous old lady, who used to visit us every now and again. Poor

Mrs. Carter was frightened of the dogs, never walked in the garden without keeping a nervous eye on Matilda and nearly had a fit when Possy paid her a courtesy visit and sat on the end of her bed making faces and giving his soft *ka kakakaa* noises. Even Kiko, that smallest and gentlest of monkeys, frightened her, and the mere suggestion of Kaa threw her into a frightful tizzy. I expect our parents thought she went on in a silly, exaggerated way, but they were fond of her, and so, in a way, were we, but we could not help teasing her sometimes. Mother made us promise that we would *never* bring Kaa into any of the little jokes we played on her, because she would most certainly have hysterics.

Mrs. Carter walked about the garden, looking nervously in all directions, and one day she wandered toward one end of the garden where Garth had dug a big hole, which he called his "mine." Down there he would let off bunches of those red Chinese crackers—blasting, he called it. He was really a kind boy, but he simply could not resist playing jokes on Mrs. Carter, so when she neared his mine he hopped down it and hid there, giving some mysterious hollow groans, and when the old lady peered nervously into the hole he let off a bunch of crackers! Mrs. Carter leaped into the air with a squeal, and then of course she was furious and refused to speak to him, and went huffily back into the house and told our father. Then Father was very angry, and said that we could not have our circus. I cried, and he relented because, after all, I had not done anything. Poor Garth was very upset; then Mrs. Carter forgave him and, anxious to show her how sorry he was, he insisted on making her the guest of honor at his birthday circus, and the old lady was most flattered.

A few days before the circus we took the Clydesdale out of the yard and pushed the hay back in the loft so as to put a bench in front of the open loft doors. Then we tidied away the horse rugs and other paraphernalia downstairs, and put up a trestle table and folding chairs for the guests to sit on. We wondered how we were going to get Mrs. Carter up the little ladder to the loft, and Garth said she would be sure to shut herself up in the folding chairs. Then he decided that, as guest of honor, Mrs. Carter must have a special chair; so he borrowed a wheelbarrow and trundled it up to the yard with a wicker armchair and cushions in it. He was hot and tired when he got there, but he had that smug look people get when they feel that whatever they have done in the past has been atoned for. He put the chair at the top of the table, settled the cushions with proud pats, and that was that—or so he thought.

We were up early on the day of the circus. All the performers had to be in the yard, and Benny had two baths, because he promptly went out and rolled in something smelly after the first one and had to be bathed again. Algy had to be fished out from under the bed and dragged to the tub, where he stood like an outraged martyr while I scrubbed the padded wrinkles of his blessed bulldog face with a soft old toothbrush. He always behaved as if he thought that a bath was a booby trap that would be sure to go off when he got in it! But once the deed was done he rather liked himself. Ajax was so big that I had to wash him in two sections, first with his front half in the tub and then with his back half.

Buck was as groomed as his shaggy little body would allow. Even Matilda was brushed. Kiko did not need touching, he was always sweet and clean; and I rubbed an oily rag over Kaa's beautifully patterned coils until he was quite a dandy, though a very sleepy one. I could not lift him straight off the ground, but had to drape him round my shoulders and then lift the rest of him. I staggered up to the yard with him festooned about me, and looked around for somewhere to park him until it was time to take him into the ring to do his act with me—and I only hoped that, as my parents would be taking it quite calmly, Mrs. Carter would not have a fit. There was an old tree stump just outside the yard, filled with crumbled bark and earth and sprouting a few leafy twigs for shade, and that seemed a good place to put the sleepy, full-fed Kaa. I curled him round carefully, glad to be rid of his weight, and then left him in peace while I went back for Matilda.

The audience in the dress circle numbered six: Mrs.

Carter, our parents, Nessie—once our nurse and now the housekeeper—Brownie and the bookkeeper, a young man who was almost as nervous of us as Mrs. Carter was. Lewis, of course, was to help us in the ring.

Benny had a large bow on his neck, and after a few wild moments of trying to chew it off he seemed to take to it and kept peering back at the ends of the bow to make sure it was there. I had made clown's caps and ruffs for Ajax and Algy out of crinkled paper. First I dressed the bewildered Algy and fastened his clown's hat on with elastic. He was very embarrassed, snorted and licked my hands and pretended to have a sneezing fit as he tried to remove the hat and frill without hurting my feelings. Then I called Ajax, and no one can tell me that dogs do not laugh! If they do not, then what was it that Algy did when he looked at Ajax? Ajax stood like an imposing statue suffering a New Year's celebration indignity as I put his cap and frill on, and Algy's face simply split in half! Algy finally wore his decorations meekly, but Ajax tore his hat and frill off and chewed them to pulp.

We got the audience seated—Mrs. Carter had to be pushed up the ladder fore and aft but finally she made it—and then we began our program. I stood in the middle of the ring with a long stock whip in my hand, while Garth, dressed as an Indian, cantered around standing up on Buck's fat little rump. Then Benny and Kiko rode Buck all by themselves, though between the large bows on Benny's neck and on Kiko's too the little monkey was practically hidden.

After that we took turns riding the calves we had tethered outside, sitting facing their tails in the approved bush style and getting well thrown for our pains. Then Matilda hopped in, and she and Garth wrestled, which they both always enjoyed. Matilda caught the boy in a firm grip and seemed to be trying to peer into his eye before she suddenly let him go, poked him in the tummy with her long toe and then hopped gracefully away! Garth laughed so much he had to sit down to get over it, and the audience clapped loudly.

After that there were several more acts, and I put on my Eastern costume for my snake-charming act. I ran to the stump to get Kaa, and he was not there. I searched for him, but there were no signs of him anywhere, so I went into the ring and did what I hoped was an Indian dance to the music of the gramophone which we had installed in the shed.

My act was the last one, and after the applause I went into the lower room where the party was all laid out on the trestle table, with the chairs set primly around and the large wicker chair standing imposingly at the end of the table waiting for the guest of honor to take it.

My father's feet appeared on the top rungs of the ladder, then Mrs. Carter's prim black shoes, as he steadied her to the accompaniment of her little squeals.

In a moment they would be right in the room, and then my eye caught sight of something queer about the wicker chair—I could not believe it. I looked again, and it was true. There, curled round the seat, was Kaa, a sure passport to hysteria for Mrs. Carter! I knew that she would think we had arranged this; Garth would be so upset and our parents very angry indeed.

Kaa was sleeping blissfully, and in an instant it would be too late to do anything, for he was so heavy I could never get him out before he was seen and the whole party became a dismal failure. I could think of only one thing to do: I snatched off my Indian shawl, spread it over Kaa and lowered myself gently onto his coils. He barely moved, he was used to my sitting on him and obligingly shifted a little so that I could sit comfortably. I clung to the arms of the chair, terrified that he would decide to come out from under the shawl and spoil everything. I kept very still and sat looking very red-faced and nervous.

Mrs. Carter and my father stepped down into the room, while the rest of the party climbed down. My father turned to face me and called, "Hullo! What are you doing at the head of the table? Come on, get off the best chair, you little monkey!"

I was speechless, and Garth came in.

"Hey!" he said, "I carried that chair up here for Mrs. Carter, not for you!"

Mrs. Carter walked toward me, and I was so terrified

I burst out, "Oh, Mrs. Carter, do *please* let me sit here. I—I do really want to so much!"

My father began to say "Nonsense!" and Garth came toward me as if he was going to pull me off the chair, when the old lady saved herself and sat down graciously at the other end of the table, saying, "Of course, dear. No, please don't move her. Why, the child was the star of the show, so she should have the star's seat!"

I felt awful. Garth was glaring at me furiously, everyone else looked very disapproving, and they determined to ignore me completely. I was so miserable, and then Kaa began to move and heaved me up and down.

Nessie said sharply, "Little girls should sit still at table!"

And how I wished I could! Garth sat alternately glaring at me and beaming at the thick icing on his cake. Then during one glare I saw his expression change, and I felt a soft *tap-tap* up my back, as Kaa uncoiled his head and neck and began mildly feeling his way up my spine. I sat quite still, wondering what the result would be if his flat head and lidless eyes suddenly peered over my shoulder. But by now I had an ally; my brother understood, and it was his turn to look horrified. He hurriedly shoved the cake into his mouth, and to my relief I felt Kaa's head slide down. The restless coils settled and I knew he would keep quiet for a little while longer, even though I had been heaving

up and down while everyone glared at me and said,
"Keep still."

It was a great relief when tea was over and the
grownups began moving toward the car. I still sat as
if I were nailed to the seat of the throne of honor. My
parents looked rather surprised, but decided that if I
was determined to behave so badly, they would simply
ignore me. Finally the last one filed out, leaving Nessie,
Lewis and Garth with me. I began to sob miserably,
but I soon perked up when I showed the sleeping Kaa
and was told that I had done exactly the right thing,
and that my mother and father would be very proud
of me when they knew.

CHAPTER XIII

# LUCK TAKES A HAND

W ITH my brother's return to school the old worry about being sent off to boarding school myself after the midwinter vacation, which meant about the end of July, began to crowd in on me once again. The thought of leaving my home, my dogs, all the people I loved, was so dreadful to me that I could not speak about it even to my mother.

I think both she and Brownie understood this, but my father insisted that for my own sake I must go where I could be among other children, and neither of them knew how to comfort me. I spent every minute of the day when I could be alone in slipping away with the dogs, going again and again to all our favorite haunts, and a great deal of the nights lying awake in my veranda bed while the sounds I loved came through the velvety night air—the call of a possum, the wail of a dingo, or the steady, surging sound of yarded cattle, all a part of my short life and almost as dear to me as Algy's loud snorings, which never disturbed me in the least. I would lie with my hand over the edge of the bed touching Ajax's great head, feeling Benny's warm lit-

146

tle body on my feet, and with my heart full of desolation and foreboding.

The dogs and I once did some fishing—not fishing as you know it, but a rather more dangerous game. In our game fishing waters were replaced by an old, dried-up well. The fishing line and the bait were a silk handkerchief, and the fish were the deadly Australian black snakes.

These snakes grow to about seven or eight feet long. They are very poisonous, but like most wild creatures, they are only dangerous if you frighten them. I always worried a lot that the dogs might attack one, but as they were used to Kaa and I had tried to teach them to leave other snakes alone, they were fairly safe. Once I saw Algy sniffing about a patch of grass, and a black snake reared itself up out of it with its tongue flickering almost on Algy's snub nose. I was afraid to call out in case he might turn to me and the snake would strike, so I stayed quite still and the snake doubled back on itself and disappeared—perhaps it could not bear to bite that silly, friendly, darling dog!

It was Lewis who showed me how to fish for snakes in the old well. The well was about fifteen feet deep with only about an inch of water at the bottom. The sides were faced with old planks, and tufts of grass grew where the boards had rotted away. The sides were dotted here and there with small round holes. We kept very quiet, and presently a flat head, with dull eyes

Lewis showed me how to fish for snakes.

and flickering tongue, poked out of one of the holes. When the head was well out Lewis lowered a silk handkerchief cornerwise to the snake. As the tip touched it the snake dodged back into its hole, but when it put its head out Lewis bobbed the handkerchief up and down and in a flash the snake struck. Lewis jerked the hanky, the snake ducked its head back, and one of its poison fangs came up in the end of the hanky.

My fishing was not so successful, but I had a lot of fun trying. Of course I knew that I should not fish without Lewis, but one day I did. Peering into the well, I saw two heads, and this was too much for me. I ran home and got one of my father's big silk handkerchiefs—Brownie always polished my hair with it— tied a piece of string to the corner and began fishing.

I missed three catches and became very absorbed in what I was doing. Then I heard a yelp and a sliding, scratching sound, lumps of soil fell into the well, and the head I was fishing for disappeared. I looked up; to my horror Ben was halfway down the well, digging his claws in, but sliding very quickly toward the bottom in a shower of rubble.

Algy began whining and scratching at the rim, and Ben, on the bottom by now and quite unhurt, barked furiously for help and danced about on his short hind legs that always seemed to have furry knickers covering his tiny hams. He peered upward and scolded me for all he was worth.

I was very worried. I did not know how to get Ben up, nor did I know how many snakes were down that well, nor how long they would stand the rumpus Ben was making. I dragged Algy to a stump and tied him up with my belt and had to scold him to make him stay there. Poor old fellow! He was very bewildered—he knew he was only trying to help Ben. Then Ajax and I raced for Lewis, who was busy carpentering. He went into his tool shed and brought out a piece of supple greased rope and we hurried back to the well.

We found Benny simply hoarse with rage at being deserted.

Lewis set to work to lasso him, but he was no help at all in his own rescue, dancing and wriggling and trying to avoid the lasso, while all the time I held my breath and watched for a deadly head and lissome body to appear from one of the holes. Finally Lewis did get the noose round the ungrateful little dog, and he was hauled up, gasping for breath as the rope tightened round his chest. Once up, he scolded and growled at everybody and was not at all grateful for being saved.

After that the well was boarded up, and the dogs and I had to go back to river fishing. The river was very low, and in patches it was so thick with riverweed that I had to use the oar like a long pole to get through. Algy, who hated water, evidently thought the weed was grass, because one day I heard a great splash behind me and Algy came to the surface draped in weeds like some river monster, gasping and very frightened, and I managed to haul him into the boat, shipping gallons of weedy water at the same time. Poor Algy! He never made the same mistake again.

One of our odd-job men was an Aborigine who called himself King Billy. He used to chop wood—when he could not help himself—and he wore a strange costume, his everyday rags topped by an old black silk top hat given to him by my English grandfather. Billy loved it, and when he wore it he changed his title from King to General, as a compliment to my grandfather and his regiment!

Billy was an expert fisherman in the Abo style, with long spears instead of hooks and lines. He would push the boat into shallow water, stand in the prow, spot a fish and throw the spear with beautiful accuracy. This way the fish is pinned to the bed of the river and the quivering shaft is there to mark the spot. My fishing in this way was not very good, but I enjoyed trying, and I *was* rather handicapped: Ajax kept quiet in the boat, but those sterling hunters Ben and Algy rushed from side to side, which made it difficult to balance a spear and myself.

When Billy was fishing I kept the dogs quiet, but they fussed so when Billy tried to hold them that I found it easier to accept the handicap. One day, when I saw a big fish swimming lazily by, I launched the spear—and myself as well! I made an awful flop and

Ajax jumped in after me, while the other two rushed to the side of the boat and nearly turned it over. In the end I clambered in, in spite of the loving kisses from Algy and Ben and the fuss they made over me, which kept pushing me back into the water again.

Those strange Australian creatures, the platypuses, funny little throwbacks to another age, were very plentiful every now and again in our river. The platypus is shy and is protected by law, but the high price of its fur makes poaching go on. From earlier days my parents had a rug of platypus skins; it was a short fur, brownish gray and very hard-wearing, rather like beaver.

Sometimes, lazing about on the quiet reaches of the river, I have seen half a dozen platypuses floating quietly on the surface, oblongs of brown fur. At the slightest movement they would flip their bodies beneath the water in a flash. They are about a foot long, with duck bills and webbed feet with spurs on the back ones—these are said to be poisonous. They build their nests in a sort of tunnel dug right up through the roots of the large trees edging the banks. Their babies are born in winter, usually two at a time, and are like smooth, fat, whitish grubs.

The time to find the nests is when a white frost is on the ground, early on a winter's morning. Then Lewis would take me along the bank, the grass blades, little javelins of ice, sticking through my sandals, until we saw a small circle of grass without frost, always near the trunk of a tree. Then Lewis began a careful digging, and the dogs had to be restrained from helping, because to disturb a platypus nest roughly may make the mother desert the babies.

We scooped the last of the earth away with our hands very gently, and there, on a nest of soil and sticks, lay two tiny babies, fat and helpless. When we had seen them we would replace the sticks, leaves and earth very carefully indeed. Platypuses have become more and more scarce, for they are gentle, defenseless creatures, and their only weapon is their speed.

Life was lazily full of the things I loved, and I would have been well content but for the lurking misery that hung over everything when I remembered suddenly that in a few months I would be far away from all this. Then one mail day, which only happened twice a week, I came walking home at sunset and saw my mother in the distance coming toward me. We met and she turned to walk back with me, and told me that my father had had a letter from the school—it had been impossible to find a vacancy for me until the new year. I was saved, at least temporarily, and that night I slept soundly without long wakeful hours of misery and weeping.

# CHAPTER XIV

# A DESPERATE ADVENTURE

AUSTRALIA is such a land of extremes that it is difficult to know whether floods or droughts are the worst, but I think that living through a really bad drought is about as nasty a thing as you can imagine. People living on stations depend on the rivers for everything except drinking water, which is caught from the rain on iron roofs and drained off into tanks. In a long drought fruit trees and vegetables die, and of course there are no flowers. What little water there is in the tanks has to be kept only for drinking, and even washing-up water and water used for tea or cooking have to be boiled river water, hauled daily and kept in big barrels. The river itself becomes horrible, just a chain of stagnant pools, more like a weed-choked lake than a river, all green and slimy and full of dead river creatures.

Animals suffer badly, droves of stock die of thirst and starvation, and the barren earth is dotted with bodies, so that a dreadful smell of death lies over the land. Although there are frequent short droughts, the long droughts only happen now and again. Then there is great danger of fire, for every blade of grass, every tree and piece of fallen timber becomes tinder ready to blaze at the slightest spark—perhaps from lightning, or from the sun shining on a piece of broken glass, or from ash dropped by a careless smoker.

I remember a drought like this when the brazen heat of the sun poured down week after week, month after month, and the air was thick and smoke-filled from far-off fires. Even poor old Algy, who hated water, would throw himself panting into the still, weedy edge of the river for coolness, and rise again looking like a bunyip, the Aborigines' fabulous river monster.

The biggest drought I remember began around Inverell, which was about seventy miles from Gunyan. When the annual show time came round the townspeople decided to go on with it in spite of the bad season, and although it was very poorly attended, there were the usual merry-go-rounds, side shows and a big circus. Then a tragedy happened; the circus was almost destroyed by fire. Some of the animals were burned in their cages, and others escaped, all of which were recaptured except three wolves, which disappeared into the wild country round about. Hunts were organized, and occasionally farmers reported raided fowl houses. One man said he saw three gaunt gray forms leap over his henhouse fence, and that he fired at the last one and thought, from the trail of blood it left, that he must have shot it in the hind leg. The poor brutes must have been very hungry, for there is not much to eat in a droughty land, and when nothing was heard of them for some weeks people thought they must have moved up north where there were more food and less vigilance.

As the drought spread round my home, my father was busy hiring drovers to move the stock on agisted land, where the owners got so much a head for the grazing rights when they had the luck to have more rain than their neighbors. Droughts were particularly hard on the small landowners. Gunyan was a big station with an area of about a hundred square miles, so there was usually some corner of it where a little feed could be found; but about fourteen miles above Gunyan a nice English couple who had bought a block of land was having a very bad time. My parents helped where they could, sending meat and vegetables to them as long as we had any.

Then Mrs. Graham, the wife of this new squatter, sent my mother a note to say that she had been unexpectedly landed with her sister's children, two little girls, one about my own age and one younger, while their mother went into the hospital for a few weeks. She begged my mother to let me stay with them for the week end. The children were homesick and miserable and she thought it would make a great difference to them to have another child to play with. But would I please leave the dogs at home, as there was always trouble between them and Mr. Graham's thoroughbred

cattle dogs, and right now they simply could not have
the dogs put out of action in the struggle to move the
drought-stricken stock.

Of course I did not want to go. I hated the thought
of leaving the dogs, and I was rather scared of the
children. Also, the wonderful reprieve I had had from
boarding school in July was running out, and only another two months remained before I was to be sent as
a boarder to the Armidale girls' school. Back had come
all the worrying and fretting, the long tearful nights
filled with dreadful anticipations of homesickness and
longing for my dogs.

However, in the circumstances my mother thought
that I should go to the Grahams', and very reluctantly
I agreed. It was arranged for me to ride over on Fri-
day afternoon and back on Sunday. Mr. Graham said
he would ride halfway to meet me, which I privately
thought was rather silly, as I was used to riding alone
much greater distances than the fourteen miles between
Gunyan and Baroona.

I was very miserable about Ajax, Ben and Algy—it
seemed to me that I had so little time left with them
that it was dreadful to have to give up two whole days
of it. My going away meant that they would have to be
shut up in a big, airy stable at night so that they could
not follow me, and in the daytime my mother promised
to keep them about the house with her. But anyway I
hated the thought. Benny would be all right; he was so

vain and self-important that he would rather enjoy howling for me and being comforted by my mother and allowed all sorts of little privileges he did not get when I was home. I pictured Algy's lined bulldog face with its flat nose pressed against the wire netting that covered the veranda, sitting patiently hour after hour, waiting for my return. But Ajax, my splendid half dingo of a dog, would be filled with the savage despair that always took possession of him when he was out of my sight, and there was nothing anyone could do that would comfort him, and I felt he was paying far too great a price for the pleasure of two silly little stranger girls.

Still, I was made to go, and there was just nothing I could do about it. So I said a sad good-by to my boys as I shut them into the stable with plenty of outsized bones, their own blankets, my blue woolen dressing gown, which they all loved and always managed to pull off my bed, and a promise from Brownie and my mother to make all the fuss they could of them.

As I had outgrown Buck I rode my beautiful chestnut mare Belle, who was as lively as Buck was sluggish and considerably more fun to ride. I rode off miserably enough, thinking about the dogs, followed by Benny's and Algy's yaps and howls and Ajax's deep cry, as long as I was within earshot. The earth was barren along the way, and it was very hot. Mr. Graham met me, and by the time we reached the house and I had been introduced to Kathleen and Enid and had a sumptuous piece of thickly iced chocolate cake, I felt just a little better.

If I had not been so worried about the dogs, it would have been a very happy week end, because after the first shyness had worn off the little girls and I got on splendidly, and Mrs. Graham said they might come to Gunyan for the next week end. I smiled when I thought how cross Buck would be when he found out what was in store for him! Mrs. Graham was very nice about the dogs and told me she was so sorry she had to ask me to leave them behind; but I did see why, Algy and Ajax were so large, and they were often very naughty about fighting.

We woke on Sunday morning to find the air searing hot and black rolling clouds of smoke on the horizon. The dry, scorching wind brought charred particles of wood and dead insects into the house. That dread thing, a bush fire, had started in an upper paddock. Mr. Graham got his few men together, and they left to fight it. He said he would be back by five o'clock, so as to ride part way home with me, which would give me time to get back before it was dark, about eight. Mrs. Graham wanted me to wait until Monday, but as there was no telephone between Baroona and Gunyan I knew my parents would worry; besides, I did not want to leave the dogs any longer. So in the end she agreed I could go, especially as none of the men could be spared to take a message, and when my father knew about the fire he would be sure to send some help, which was badly needed.

It was after five that we saw a horseman coming slowly toward us. He was a son of one of the stockmen, a boy of about sixteen, utterly exhausted, his eyes blood-red from the smoke and his hair and eyebrows singed by the flames he had been fighting. Mrs. Graham gave him a cool drink and made him sit down. Then he told us that Mr. Graham simply could not leave the fire, and he must keep every hand with him. He had sent George back to get the spring cart and to bring back drinking water and food in it, as they must stay there all night.

The fire had gained so much way that when night fell the sky glowed with it, and my parents would be very anxious if I had not reached home. Mr. Graham needed help more than ever, and Mrs. Graham, worried to distraction as she was, finally agreed that it was rather silly to insist on anyone going halfway with me when I was used to riding anywhere I chose by myself and I knew every inch of the way—including a short cut, which I had not taken on my way over for fear of missing Mr. Graham.

It was nearly six o'clock by the time I rode away, leaving Mrs. Graham bustling about the kitchen, helped by the girls, getting the food and drink ready for the fire fighters. I rode off at a brisk canter, hurrying to get home before my parents began to worry about me.

A couple of miles from Baroona I decided to turn off the rough bush track I was following and to take the short cut I knew about. Then a few miles from the turnoff I found that a new wire fence had been put up since I had been that way months before. It was a nuisance, as the short cut would only have saved a couple of miles, and the wire fence would delay me longer than it would take to ride that far. Still, there was nothing for it, I could not get through or over the wire. There was a post-and-rail fence a mile or two away from the direction I was going in, however, and I decided it would be shorter to follow the wire fence up to this, because I was sure I could pull a top rail off somewhere and then jump Belle over the lower one, and this way I would soon make up the extra distance.

When I did reach the rail fence I had an awful job pulling out a rail—I simply was not strong enough—but finally I managed it and got Belle over the lower rail. Then I had to replace the heavy top one in case some of the stock got through, and this took a long time too. When I finished this it was beginning to get dark with that swift completeness that is typical of Australia, when you are left feeling like a bird in a cage over which a dark cover has been flung.

I hurried Belle along and we cantered over the brown, shriveled ground. I could not see where I was riding, but I knew that Belle would take me in the general direction of home. Once I heard the bloodcurdling, mournful howl of a dingo from the dry bed of a small gulley on my left, and on top of the bank I thought that for a moment I saw the animal's glowing eyes. I urged Belle on. I was not frightened of dingoes; deadly as they are to stock, I had never heard of their attacking humans, and they never hunt in packs. A whole family of dingoes may stick together for a while when the pups are young, but once they grow up dingoes become lone hunters.

Belle was almost galloping when suddenly I felt her lurch forward. She hit the ground and I must have sailed over her head and knocked myself out, for all I remember is a sharp pain in my shoulder, then complete darkness. After goodness knows how long, I began a slow coming-to from some cold, black, faraway place of the senses.

I tried to sit up, but the sharp pain in my left shoulder made me stop. My left ankle hurt dreadfully, and my head throbbed, so that I seemed to be seeing everything in a blur, for the bright starlight made it possible to see the blurred outlines of a few tree stumps that were around me.

Again I heard that mournful, wavering howl from somewhere in the darkness, and my throbbing scalp prickled with a fear I did not understand. I realized that I must try and do something, but I did not know exactly what. There was no sign of Belle, but I could see only a few yards into the darkness, and, anyway, by the dreadful pain in my shoulder I guessed something must have broken, and I would never be able to mount the mare. I hoped that she was all right and that she would make for home, because then a search party would come for me and Ajax would find me very quickly. I knew that the mare must have stepped into a rabbit hole and come down herself and probably thrown me some distance, and I only prayed that she had not broken a leg and was not lying somewhere just out of my sight, suffering miserably.

Suddenly a pair of eyes shone greenly in the darkness a few yards away, then another pair appeared beside the first—and another! I was afraid. I felt a small stick under my hand and tried to throw it. The movement hurt dreadfully, but the three pairs of eyes disappeared, only to reappear a few yards farther to my right. It was painful to turn my head, but I did, and saw a twisted tree a few yards behind me. Setting my teeth, I dragged myself along the ground toward it. I knew I could not climb into it, but at least it was something solid at my back, and I felt a slowly growing fear of those burning green eyes.

I could only move a few inches at a time, and my face was wet with pain and exertion. Then I must have fainted because I came to with a horrible animal smell in my nostrils. I opened my eyes and stared straight into a pair of glaring eyes above a long dark muzzle. I yelled, and the gaunt form leaped backward. Then

I saw that it was not a dingo; it was much taller and rangier than any full-blooded dingo could be, and it had not the dingo's characteristic golden coat that turns to a pale silver by starlight. This creature had been a shaggy dark gray—and suddenly I knew that those three pairs of eyes belonged to the wolves that had escaped from the circus.

My heart leaped with terror. The small movements I made kept them back for the moment, but they would not do so for long, and I had no way to defend myself. I doubted that I could even get as far as the tree, and, anyway, it would not help. The wolves were hungry; they had been ranging a drought-stricken country where game had vanished. So what chance did a badly injured girl have against three of them maddened with hunger?

I wanted to cry, but somehow that seemed such a useless thing to do that I kept my tears back. As usual when I was in trouble I thought of Ajax. I had always known that between my dog and me there was some strange instinct that told us when the other one was in trouble. Whatever it was, I believed that something would tell Ajax that I was in great need of him and that he would come to me, and I raised my voice and called as loudly as I could, "Ajax! Ajax! Come to me—I need you!"

Now that my eyes were used to the darkness and the fierce, stabbing pains in my head were a little better, I could see the three lean, hungry forms moving round me in circles, round and round, frightening shadows that circled monotonously, always closing in a little. Their eyes gleamed as they turned their heads in the starlight, going round and round and round in the way the Red Indians circled encampments of covered wagons in the frontier days.

I began to feel lightheaded; it was a nightmare watching those silent forms circling, circling. I noticed that the one bringing up the rear did not lope silently like the other two, for he limped badly and made a small, dry, rustling sound as his lame foot dragged a little on the parched ground.

Suddenly they stopped circling and threw their heads up, and the hungry, mournful cry I heard earlier came from their shaggy throats. Again my scalp prickled, but I had passed the apex of my terror, and now in all the pain and confusion I seemed to be standing outside my body and watching those poor, famished beasts in a way that seemed to be unconnected with my own danger. Their wails died away, and they began their endless circling again—then one broke from the circle and rushed toward me. I did not make a conscious movement; without my will my right foot kicked out and the wolf leaped back. The pain of the movement was terrible, and I thought that I was fainting again and tried desperately not to, staring hard at the three forms, and as the faintness passed away I noticed that the circling had stopped and all three beasts were standing with their backs to me, listening intently to something I could not hear.

And then I did hear something, a sound that meant life itself to me—the thud of great feet on the dry earth—and Ajax leaped out of the darkness to my side and put his golden muzzle for an instant against my face before he whirled to face my three enemies.

The wolves had turned too and stood facing us, the leader slightly in advance and one wolf on each side of him. Now my fears for myself turned to a sickening, desperate fear for Ajax. Those great, gaunt, hunger-ridden bodies, the long cruel heads, were filled with the power and savagery of the wild. They were the most terrible enemies my dog had ever faced. Ajax was taller and heavier than the largest wolf, but there were three of them, and they were all crazed with hunger. There was nothing I could do.

Ajax breathed deeply and evenly as he always did before a fight, and the only sound he made was a sort of faint, shuddering growl deep in his chest. The wolves were quite silent, their eyes gleaming in the starlight. The leader took a stiff-legged step forward. The others followed him and I felt Ajax move forward from me. Again that small movement forward, and I knew that my Ajax was steady as a rock and balanced to meet the swiftest rush with all the cunning and power of his own wild ancestors pitted against the

The wolves turned and stood facing him.

167

deadly, pack-fighting knowledge of the strangers. Then
the leader rushed forward with incredible swiftness,
his head low, his jaws aimed for Ajax's front legs to
cripple him, while the other two sprang higher to bear
him down with their weight. Ajax was ready for them;
he leaped sideways, his quick slash ripped the leader's
shoulder wide open, and the leaping blood shone dark
in the starlight.

Then I found I could not follow the fight in the half
light. There was no sound except the breathing of the
fighters and the clash of teeth when a savage slash
missed the flesh. I saw a great gray form go hurtling
through the air and lie still, but Ajax and the leader
fought on, while the lame wolf kept darting in, slashing
at Ajax and leaping clumsily back again. Ajax must
have decided to end these harrying tactics from the
rear, for as the lame wolf retreated from one attack
behind its leader, Ajax gave a great leap right over
the leader's head, and with a crunch of his jaws he left
the lame wolf on the ground and whirled round to take
the leader's return rush.

Sometimes I closed my eyes to shut out these grim,
struggling figures fighting, as it seemed to me, for an
eternity. But all the time my ears were filled with the
dry sound of their rushing feet, the gasps and thuds of
body on body, the clash and snap of jaws, their heavy,
labored breathing. . . . Would it never end? I began
to despair.

My eyes were shut tight when suddenly the sounds of the struggle stopped and I felt heavy breathing against my face. For an instant I was in a panic and could not open my eyes. Then I opened them and saw a great, bloodstained form beside me, slashed and torn and with one leg badly mangled—Ajax. I pressed my face against his reddened muzzle and cried bitterly as I had not been able to cry for myself, and I knew that in his own way he was telling me that all was well.

Around me I could see the big forms of the three fallen wolves, and as I stopped sobbing Ajax limped over to the leader, sniffed at him and then raised his muzzle to the sky to give his long, wavering call of victory, a call that was akin to the hunger cries the wolves had given earlier on. I could not struggle any more. I slumped down onto the ground and Ajax lay beside me, and it was like that my father and Lewis found us.

They told me that Ajax had become very restless about dusk and that as soon as Belle arrived home trailing her bridle they let Ajax out of the stable and he was off in a flash on Belle's trail, far ahead of them before they could get the horses saddled, collect torches and make a slower progress. Belle's tracks were not easy to follow on the hard, dry earth and with no light but the torches.

They heard Ajax's victorious cry and found us a few minutes afterward, stumbling first over the body of one wolf before they saw the other two, and then Ajax, close beside me.

Now that the excitement was over, the pain was really bad, and the men picked me up and put a pad under my left arm to ease the pain from my broken collarbone. They could do nothing about my badly twisted ankle, or what proved to be slight concussion, which began to affect my eyesight. Lewis tore up his handkerchief and bandaged Ajax's badly bitten leg; the other wounds had to wait. Then, carrying me very gently and with Ajax following on three legs, they turned toward home, leading the horses until they got to where it was possible to bring the car to take us the rest of the way.

There Ajax and I waited with my father, while Lewis rode quickly home, prepared my mother for the sight of me and drove the car back. My mother telephoned for the doctor. I was washed and put in my bed, and Ajax, his wounds cleaned and his leg properly attended to, lay beside me on the veranda.

My mother insisted that I should be kept very quiet, but I could hear my father and Lewis talking in the room next to me.

Lewis said, "So that's what happened to the three wolves from the circus. Queer their coming down into the droughty country——"

"I suppose the number of people hunting for them up north made it even harder for them to get food."

"Yes. I'll get the skins tomorrow. You may as well have something out of this. Let Ajax lie on a rug made of his enemies."

"Ajax—there isn't anything in the world that Ajax wants and I can give him that he can't have."

I knew that Lewis was smiling as he said, "The nice thing about Ajax is that he *has* what he wants, and he is prepared to die to keep it!"

After a time the doctor came and the next hour was pretty bad for me; the setting of the collarbone and the touching of my ankle hurt a great deal, and the pain made me wide awake instead of sleepy. I could not make a fuss, because if I had, Ajax would have stopped the doctor from touching me. As it was he did not like it very much, but it took my mind off myself to try and keep him from worrying—and he had certainly earned it.

When the doctor finished, my mother stayed on with me, and the doctor went in to talk to my father. Their voices came clearly out onto the veranda, and I heard something that seemed to make it all worth while.

I heard the doctor say firmly to my father, "The child's tough enough. Physically she'll be all right as soon as that collarbone sets, but she has had a terrible shock and it may take her years to get over it. Of course you must give up the idea of sending her away to school, probably for years. Keep her at home where she's happy—never mind about anything else. She's been fretting about boarding school, I know, and it must stop. She must not have anything to worry her until she is quite over this.

I looked at my mother and she smiled down at me. Indeed it had been worth it, and I felt that Ajax would think so too.

I put my hand over the edge of the bed and touched the gaunt, silken head of my dog Ajax, slashed and marred in my defense. On my other side Algy snored loudly, and in the crook of my sound arm little Ben, the mighty hunter, yipped in his dreams. I went to sleep with the sound, the sight, the security of my world all around me—undisturbed and beautiful.